PRENTICE HALL MATHEMATICS

ALGEBRA 1
GEOMETRY
ALGEBRA 2

TI-83/84 PLUS
Activities

Laurie E. Bass, Allan E. Bellman, Art Johnson

PEARSON
Prentice
Hall

Needham, Massachusetts
Upper Saddle River, New Jersey

ISBN: 0-13-125164-3
3 4 5 6 7 8 9 10   07 06 05 04

TI-83/84 Plus Activities

Contents

*For Chapters 1–7, see also "Topics in Algebra 1 Apps," pp. xix–xx.

Introduction

Activities and the compact disc (CD) in this booklet accompany lessons from the Prentice Hall textbooks *Algebra 1, Geometry,* and *Algebra 2.*

The Activities have been designed for use with Texas Instruments (TI) handheld technology, specifically the TI-84 Plus, TI-84 Plus Silver Edition, TI-83 Plus, and TI-83 Plus Silver Edition handheld devices. (In this booklet, "TI-83/84 Plus" refers to all four devices.) The Activities also use TI Apps and Prentice Hall programs.

Apps   TI's Handheld Software Applications (Apps) provide added functionality, such as the ability to construct geometric figures.

Programs   The Prentice Hall programs provide further enhancements to functionality. A special type of program called an *AppVar* can run only when its corresponding App is running.

Activities and Teacher Notes

- You can use the Activities in this booklet (and on the accompanying CD) to introduce, investigate, and extend the ideas of the lessons in *Algebra 1, Geometry,* and *Algebra 2*. Students can work individually with their calculators, but you can invite them to share discoveries as they proceed.

- You can use the Teacher Notes for each Activity to find out more about the Activity, including answers to Activity exercises.

The Accompanying CD

The CD, in the sleeve inside the back cover, includes:

- Activities and Teacher Notes from this booklet in print-ready form.

- Apps and programs (including AppVars) needed for the Activities.

- A User's Guide for each App.

- StudyCards™ stacks for practice and review of each chapter of the textbooks.

- Data lists for exercises in the *Algebra 1* and *Algebra 2* textbooks— a data-entry timesaver.

- A *TI Technology Guide* for detailed information about the TI Apps and related technology.

- TI Connect™ software, which allows you to work with items on the CD and lets your computer "talk" with your TI-83/84 Plus.

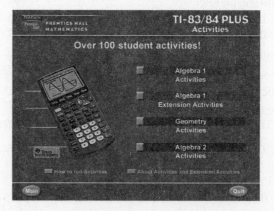

Starting an Activity

What You Need

- a computer with CD drive

- this booklet (The Activities are also in PDF format on the CD.)

- the CD on the inside back cover

- TI-83/84 Plus handheld devices for you and your students

- A TI cable (If you do not have a cable, you can obtain one from Texas Instruments. See the back cover.)

What To Do

1. Set up.

   - Install the CD on your computer. The CD includes TI Connect software.

   - Connect your computer and your TI-83/84 Plus using the TI cable. Be sure to insert each end of the cable completely.

   - Select an Activity from the booklet. At the top of the Activity page, note the files you'll need. (See pp. xiv–xvi for a complete list of files for each Activity.)

2. Run TI Connect. On your computer screen, make sure that a window is open for your TI-83/84 Plus.

3. In the "Apps & Programs" folder, find the file(s) you need. Transfer the file(s) to the window for your TI-83/84 Plus.

4. Distribute the files needed to each TI-83/84 Plus in the classroom. One way is to have students use unit-to-unit links.

5. Do the Activity.

StudyCards Stacks and Data Lists

StudyCards stacks on the CD are "electronic index cards" that provide for student self-assessment of vocabulary and concepts. Use them with the StudyCards App.

Data lists on the CD are lists that students need to have in their calculators to do several of the exercises in *Algebra 1* and *Algebra 2*. By using these data lists, students avoid having to carefully enter data by hand and therefore have more time for exploring the mathematics.

Use Steps 2–4 above to transfer StudyCards stacks and data lists to your TI-83/84 Plus.

TI Technology Guide at a Glance

The CD includes a complete *TI Technology Guide*. Here are some *Guide* topics in brief. The *Guide* gives details.

TI Connect™ Software

You install the TI Connect software on your Windows® PC or Macintosh® computer. In addition to letting you transfer files between your computer and your TI-83/84 Plus, this software enables you to view or save TI-83/84 Plus files and screen images on your computer, paste screen images into other applications, and make, display, and modify list files, number files, and matrix files.

TI-83/84 Plus Operating System

At the start of the school year, check that each TI-83/84 Plus has the current operating system (OS). With your TI-83/84 Plus connected to your computer and your computer connected to the Internet, run TI Connect. On the TI Connect screen, click on the update button. If you find that you need to update, follow the on-screen instructions.

Finding the TI-83/84 Plus Files You Need

The names of the Apps (see next page) suggest their use. The names of the programs (including AppVars) and data lists are coded, but the codes are keyed to the intended use. For example, the program A1L66B (see page 11) accompanies an *Algebra 1* Activity for Lesson 6-6. It's the second such program, after A1L66A.

You can find a correlation of Apps and programs to Activities on pp. xiv–xvi. You can find a correlation of the data lists to textbook exercises on pp. xvii–xviii.

Running an App, Program, or AppVar

For an App, press `APPS`. Select the App and press `ENTER`.

For a program (that is not an AppVar) used with an App, have the App running. Press `PRGM`. Select the program and press `ENTER` twice.

For a Cabri® Jr. AppVar, have Cabri Jr. running. Select **Open** in the Cabri Jr. F1 menu. Press `ENTER`, select the AppVar, and press `ENTER`.

For a StudyCards™ AppVar (stack), have the StudyCards App running. In the MAIN MENU, select 2: CHOOSE NEW STACK. Select the desired stack and press `ENTER`.

Note: Each Activity assumes that you have the appropriate App running from the start. If one App is active and you try to run another, you may receive an error message that prompts you to choose between the Apps.

TI-83/84 Plus Apps on the CD

Here are the TI Apps available on the CD and a brief description of each.

Cabri® Jr. (CabriJr)	provides interactive, dynamic geometry modeling. Learn more about this App on pages viii–ix.
Guess My Coefficients App (GuesCoef)	challenges students to identify the coefficients of linear, quadratic, and absolute value functions from characteristics of their graphs.
Inequality Graphing App (Inequal)	simplifies the graphing of inequalities and lets you store the coordinates of special points.
Polynomial Rootfinder and Simultaneous Equation Solver App (PolySmlt)	finds the roots (zeros) of polynomials of degree 1 through 30. It also finds solutions of systems of linear equations, or tells you that a given system has no solution or infinitely many solutions.
Probability Simulation App (Prob Sim)	simulates various games of chance for probability investigations, generates random numbers, and provides ways to summarize data.
Science Tools App (SciTools)	calculates with significant digits, converts measurements and scientific constants from one unit to another, provides ways to display data and find best-fit functions for given data, and performs basic vector operations.
Solve it! App (SolveIt)	provides practice on algebra problems at different skill levels.
StudyCards™ App (StudyCrd)	displays electronic flash cards to review key terms and concepts. Learn more about this App on pages xii–xiii.
Topics in Algebra 1 Apps	provide tutorial and practice activities for early Chapters of *Algebra 1*. Learn more about this App on pages xix–xx.
Transformation Graphing App (Transfrm)	shows and uses the effects of changing parameter values on graphs of functions. Learn more about this App on page x.

Your CD contains a complete User's Guide for each App.

StudyCards Creator

The CD also contains the TI desktop tool, StudyCards Creator for Windows PC only. It lets you make your own StudyCards stacks or change existing stacks.

Memory

Like any computer, your TI-83/84 Plus has pre-set memory capacity, with the amounts varying among the TI-84 Plus, TI-84 Plus Silver Edition, TI-83 Plus, and TI-83 Plus Silver Edition. If you try to load more than the device can hold, you will get a memory error. To learn more about memory capacity, see the *TI Technology Guide* on the CD.

Cabri® Jr.

The Cabri® Jr. application lets you construct, analyze, and transform mathematical models and geometric diagrams. Cabri Jr. was developed for TI by Cabrilog and renowned French mathematician Jean-Marie Laborde.

With Cabri Jr. you can:

- Perform analytic, transformational, and Euclidean geometric actions.

- Make geometric constructions interactively with points, lines, polygons, circles, sets of points for loci, and other basic geometric objects.

- Alter geometric objects in real time to see patterns, make conjectures, and draw conclusions.

Hints and Tips

In Cabri Jr., you can access the **F1–F5** menus by pressing the keys
`Y=` , `WINDOW` , `ZOOM` , `TRACE` , `GRAPH` just below the TI-83/84 Plus screen.
You may wish to keep this page in front of you until you become familiar with them.

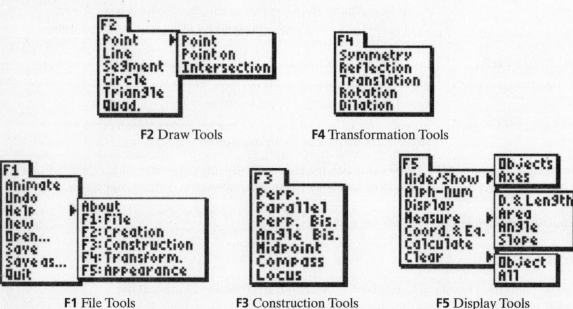

F2 Draw Tools   **F4** Transformation Tools

F1 File Tools   **F3** Construction Tools   **F5** Display Tools

The F1 Menu

Animate   Select **Animate** and press `ENTER` . Select a point that was constructed on a segment or circle. When you see the double arrow, press `ENTER` .

You can stop an animation in three ways:

1. When the animated point returns to the cursor and you see the double arrow, press `ENTER` .

2. Press `2nd` and then `ENTER` to stop all animated points.

3. Select **Undo** and press `ENTER` .

Undo   Select **Undo** and press `ENTER` .

Open...   Select **Open** and press `ENTER` to see the AppVar list.

The F2 Menu

Point Select **Point** and press `ENTER`. Move the cursor to a desired location and press `ENTER`. To construct a point on an object, be sure the object is flashing before you press `ENTER`. To construct a point at the intersection of two objects, be sure both objects are flashing.

Line or Segment Select **Line** or **Segment** and press `ENTER`. Move the cursor to a desired location for one point and press `ENTER`. Repeat for a second point.

Circle Select **Circle** and press `ENTER`. Move the cursor to a desired location for the center and press `ENTER`. Move the cursor to a desired point on the circle and press `ENTER`.

Triangle or Quadrilateral Select **Triangle** or **Quadrilateral** and press `ENTER`. For each vertex, move the cursor to the desired location and press `ENTER`.

The F3 Menu

Parallel Select **Parallel** and press `ENTER`. Select a line or segment and press `ENTER`. Use the arrows to drag the parallel line to the desired location.

To construct a parallel line through a given point, select **Parallel** and press `ENTER`. Select the point and press `ENTER`. Select the line (or segment) and press `ENTER`.

The F5 Menu

Measure Select **Measure** and then select **D & Length**, **Area**, **Angle**, or **Slope** from the submenu. Press `ENTER`. Select the object to be measured. Press `ENTER` to install the measurement.

Use the arrows to relocate an installed measurement and press `ENTER`.

Use **D & Length** to measure a side or the perimeter of a triangle or quadrilateral. Move the cursor to the figure so that the side (for length) or the entire figure (for perimeter) is flashing. (Press `2nd` to switch which is flashing.) Then press `ENTER`.

Clear Select **Clear** and then select **Object** or **All** from the submenu. Clear Object gives you an erasing cursor. To erase an object, move the cursor to the object and press `ENTER`. Clear All erases everything on the screen.

You can erase some objects without using **Clear**. With no tool active, select the object. If the cursor becomes hollow, press `DEL`.

You can also erase the screen. Press `CLEAR` three times and then press `ENTER`.

Screen Mechanics

To change or deactivate a tool, press `CLEAR`.

To drag an object, deactivate the current tool and move the cursor to the desired object. If the cursor becomes hollow, press `ALPHA`. Drag the object with the hand-shaped cursor that appears. To stop dragging, press `ENTER` or `CLEAR`.

Transformation Graphing App

Use the Transformation Graphing App to investigate how changing the parameter values A, B, C, and D affects the graphs of these functions.

$$Y = AX + B$$
linear

$$Y = A|X - B| + C$$
absolute value

$$Y = (X - A)(X - B)(X - C)$$
polynomial

$$Y = AX^2 + C$$

$$Y = AX^2 + BX$$

$$Y = AX^2 + BX + C$$

$$Y = A(X - B)^2 + C$$

quadratic (various forms)

$$Y = A\sqrt{(X - B)} + C$$
square root

$$Y = AB^X + C$$
exponential

$$Y = (A/(X - B)) + C$$
rational

$$Y = A\sin(B(X - C)) + D$$
trigonometric

Hints and Tips

Name Press **APPS**. The Transformation Graphing App is named Transfrm.

Running You can tell whether the Transformation Graphing App is active by checking the Y= screen. The App is active if you see special icons in front of Y1, Y2, etc. Note that you can select only one function at a time.

Quitting To quit the Transformation Graphing App, press **APPS**, select Transfrm, and press **ENTER**. You will see a menu with the choices 1: Uninstall and 2: Continue. Select Uninstall and press **ENTER**. (*Note*: This does not remove the App from your TI-83/84 Plus.)

Parameter Values Programs used with the Transformation Graphing App often show parameter values on the graph screen. To change a parameter value, select the parameter by highlighting its = sign using the up and down arrow keys. Type the new value and press **ENTER**.

Speed Tip: Press the right (left) arrow key to increment (decrement) parameter values by the Step value. (See **Settings**.)

Settings (Play and Play-Fast) Press **WINDOW** and the up arrow key to see the SETTINGS menu. This menu gives you a way to change the Step value and another way to change the screen parameter values. (See **Parameter Values**.)

The SETTINGS menu also shows three icons, >‖, >, >> that represent Play-Pause, Play, and Play-Fast, respectively. If you select Play or Play-Fast and press **ENTER**, Max also appears. Use Max to set the maximum value for the selected parameter.

Animate Once you have set the values for the parameters and Max (see **Settings**), press **GRAPH** to see a "slide show." The screen will cycle through graphs for values of the selected parameter from its initial value through the incremental steps to the Max value.

The slide show can show at most 13 graphs. If the screen shows a memory error, change the initial value of the parameter, the value of Max, or the size of the step to reduce the number of graphs.

To stop the slide show, press **ENTER**. To resume, press **ENTER** again. Press **ON** to go directly to the SETTINGS menu.

Inequality Graphing App

Use the Inequality Graphing App to streamline the graphing of inequalities, including graphs with vertical boundary lines. For linear programming activities, you can show the region of feasible points, trace on and store the coordinates of corner points and other points of interest, and evaluate objective functions at all such points.

Hints and Tips

Name   Press **APPS** . The Inequality Graphing App is named **Inequal**.

Graphing   On the **Y=** screen, enter an equation or view an equation entered by running a program. Select the = sign. Press **ALPHA** F2, F3, F4, or F5 for $<, \le, >,$ or $\ge,$ respectively. Then press **GRAPH** .

Shading   This App shades the solution region for each inequality. To shade an intersection (the solution of a system) or a union, use **Shades** shown on the graph screen. Press **ALPHA** F1 (or F2) to see the choices.

Quitting   To quit the Inequality Graphing App, press **APPS** , select **Inequal**, press **ENTER** , select **Quit Inequal**, and press **ENTER** .

Using DEFAULT

DEFAULT is a general program that clears the entries from the Y= screen. It also restores the standard viewing window and various general mode settings. You can load DEFAULT into the class handhelds at the beginning of your Algebra 1 or Algebra 2 course and use it throughout the year. It is good practice to run DEFAULT after you finish using any program within the Transformation Graphing or Inequality Graphing Apps.

DEFAULT does not restore = signs that you replaced in the Y= screen. See **Graphing** above.

StudyCards™ App

StudyCards™ software lets students replace the traditional practice/review stacks of index cards with electronic "cards" they can view on their TI-83/84 Plus.

You can use ready-made StudyCards stacks. You can also make your own stacks using TI's StudyCards Creator software (Windows PC only). Students can view the Stacks on their TI-83/84 Plus handhelds using the StudyCards App.

There are two ready-made stacks for each chapter of the *Algebra 1*, *Geometry*, and *Algebra 2* textbooks. Cards in the vocabulary stack suggest an idea on one side and show the correct vocabulary term on the flip side. For example:

Front side:

```
The distance of a number
from 0 on a number line is
the __ ? __ of the number.




MENU YES  NO  FLIP STAT ✛
```

FLIP side:

```
absolute value




MENU YES  NO  FLIP STAT ✛
```

Cards in the key-concepts stack give a multiple-choice conceptual question on the front side and show the correct choice and explanation on the flip side.

Front side:

```
What must be true about
numbers a, b, and c for
you to conclude ac < bc?

1) a > b, c > 0
2) a < b, c < 0
3) a > b, c < 0
4) a < b, c = 0
MENU CHOICE:? FLIP STAT ✛
```

FLIP side:

```
The correct answer is
3) a > b, c < 0.

By the Multiplication
Property of Inequality,
if a > b and c < 0, then
ac < bc.
MENU CHOICE:3 FLIP STAT ✛
```

Hints and Tips

The StudyCards App (StudyCrd) is self-explanatory and working through it is intuitive. The User's Guide is also on the CD. Here are some highlights.

Some screen menu choices:

YES	NO	CHOICE: ?	FLIP	STAT	✛
Removes card from stack.	Keeps card in stack.	Records your answer.	Turns card over.	Summarizes your success.	Shows active arrow buttons.

Other helpful tips:

- Answer a fill-in-the-blank vocabulary item mentally or on scratch paper.

- Answer a multiple-choice concept item by pressing the number of the choice.

- A correct choice removes a concept item from the stack.

- Use the right arrow key to move to the next card. Use the left arrow key to return to the previous card.

- Use the up and down arrow keys (when blinking in the screen icon) to page through screens for multiple-screen items.

After completing a stack, your options include:

REPEAT   to view the diminished stack.

START OVER   to view the complete, original stack.

```
┌──────────────────────────────┐
│   CARDS REMAINING:B          │
│ 1:REPEAT                      │
│ 2:START OVER                  │
│ 3:CHOOSE NEW STACK            │
│ 4:RESULTS                     │
│ 5:MAIN MENU                   │
│ 6:QUIT                        │
└──────────────────────────────┘
```

Using StudyCards Creator

See the StudyCards Creator User's Guide on the CD that accompanies this booklet.

Correlation of Apps and Programs to Activities

This chart shows the TI Apps and programs you need for the Activities in this booklet. For downloading convenience, it lists by chapter *all* the files that you may find useful, including StudyCards™ programs and data-list group names.

Activities for *Algebra 1*

Chap/ Lesson	Activity	TI App(s)	Program(s)
Ch. 1	StudyCards Vocabulary/Concepts	StudyCards	A1CH01MC, A1CH01SC
	TI *Topics in Algebra 1*	ALG1CH1 (Number Sense)	———
Ch. 2	StudyCards Vocabulary/Concepts	StudyCards	A1CH02MC, A1CH02SC
	TI *Topics in Algebra 1*	ALG1CH2 (Linear Equations)	———
Ch. 3	StudyCards Vocabulary/Concepts	StudyCards	A1CH03MC, A1CH03SC
	TI *Topics in Algebra 1*	ALG1CH4 (Linear Inequalities)	———
Ch. 4	StudyCards Vocabulary/Concepts	StudyCards	A1CH04MC, A1CH04SC
Ch. 5	StudyCards Vocabulary/Concepts	StudyCards	A1CH05MC, A1CH05SC
	TI *Topics in Algebra 1*	ALG1CH2 (Linear Equations)	———
5-5	Measurement Conversions	Science Tools	———
Ch. 6	StudyCards Vocabulary/Concepts	StudyCards	A1CH06MC, A1CH06SC
	Data Lists	———	A1CH06DL
	TI *Topics in Algebra 1*	ALG1CH3 (Linear Functions)	
6-2	Linear Graphs	Transformation Graphing	A1L62A
	Linear Function Match	Transformation Graphing, Guess My Coefficients	A1L62B
	Line 'Em Up	Transformation Graphing	A1L62C
6-4	Writing Equations of Lines	Guess My Coefficients	———
6-6	Trend Lines	Transformation Graphing	A1L66A, A1L66B, A1L66C
6-7	Absolute Value Graphs	Transformation Graphing	A1L67
Ch. 7	StudyCards Vocabulary/Concepts	StudyCards	A1CH07MC, A1CH07SC
	TI *Topics in Algebra 1*	ALG1CH5 (Linear Systems)	———
7-1	Tortoise and the Hare	Transformation Graphing	A1L71
7-2	Linear Systems I	Transformation Graphing	A1L72A
	Linear Systems II	Transformation Graphing	A1L72B
7-5	Linear Inequality Graphs	Inequality Graphing	
7-6	Linear Inequality Systems	Inequality Graphing	A1L76
Ch. 8	StudyCards Vocabulary/Concepts	StudyCards	A1CH08MC, A1CH08SC
	Data Lists	———	A1CH08DL
8-7	Exponential Graphs	Transformation Graphing	A1L87
8-8	Exponential Function Match	Transformation Graphing	A1L88
Ch. 9	StudyCards Vocabulary/Concepts	StudyCards	A1CH09MC, A1CH09SC
	Data Lists	———	A1CH09DL
9-3	Multiplying Binomials	Cabri® Jr.	A1L93
9-4	Square of a Binomial	Cabri Jr.	A1L94
Ch. 10	StudyCards Vocabulary/Concepts	StudyCards	A1CH10MC, A1CH10SC
	Data Lists	———	A1CH10DL
10-1	Quadratic Graphs I	Transformation Graphing	A1L101
10-2	Quadratic Graphs II	Transformation Graphing	A1L102A
	Quadratic Function Match I	Transformation Graphing	A1L102B

Activities for *Algebra 1* (continued)

10-5	Graphs, Solutions, and Factors	Transformation Graphing	A1L105
10-8	The Discriminant	Transformation Graphing	A1L108
10-9	Choose a Model I	Transformation Graphing	A1L109
Ch. 11	StudyCards Vocabulary/Concepts	StudyCards	A1CH11MC, A1CH11SC
11-6	Square Root Graphs	Transformation Graphing	A1L116A
	Square Root Function Match	Transformation Graphing	A1L116B
Ch. 12	StudyCards Vocabulary/Concepts	StudyCards	A1CH12MC, A1CH12SC
12-2	Rational Graphs	Transformation Graphing	A1L122A
	Rational Function Match	Transformation Graphing	A1L122B, A1L122C, A1L122D

Activities for *Geometry*

Chap/ Lesson	Activity	TI App(s)	Program(s)
Ch. 1	StudyCards Vocabulary/Concepts	StudyCards™	GCH01MC, GCH01SC
1-5	Perpendicular Bisectors	Cabri® Jr.	GL15A
	Angle Bisectors	Cabri Jr.	GL15B
Ch. 2	StudyCards Vocabulary/Concepts	StudyCards	GCH02MC, GCH02SC
2-4	Linear Pairs	Cabri Jr.	GL24
2-5	Vertical Angles	Cabri Jr.	GL25
Ch. 3	StudyCards Vocabulary/Concepts	StudyCards	GCH03MC, GCH03SC
3-1	Parallel Lines, Related Angles	Cabri Jr.	GL31
3-3	Exterior Angle of a Triangle	Cabri Jr.	GL33
3-4	Exterior Angle Sums	Cabri Jr.	GL34A, GL34B
Ch. 4	StudyCards Vocabulary/Concepts	StudyCards	GCH04MC, GCH04SC
4-5	Angle Bisectors in Triangles I	Cabri Jr.	GL45A
	Segment Bisectors in Triangles	Cabri Jr.	GL45B
Ch. 5	StudyCards Vocabulary/Concepts	StudyCards	GCH05MC, GCH05SC
5-1	Triangle Midsegments	Cabri Jr.	GL51
5-3	Perpendicular Bisectors in Triangles	Cabri Jr.	GL53
5-5	Inequalities in Triangles	Cabri Jr.	GL55
Ch. 6	StudyCards Vocabulary/Concepts	StudyCards	GCH06MC, GCH06SC
Ch. 7	StudyCards Vocabulary/Concepts	StudyCards	GCH07MC, GCH07SC
7-1	Area of a Triangle	Cabri Jr.	GL71A, GL71B
7-2	Triangles and Circles	Cabri Jr.	GL72A, GL72B
7-4	Areas of Rhombuses and Kites	Cabri Jr.	GL74A, GL74B
Ch. 8	StudyCards Vocabulary/Concepts	StudyCards	GCH08MC, GCH08SC
8-5	Parallel Segments in Triangles	Cabri Jr.	GL85A
	Angle Bisectors in Triangles II	Cabri Jr.	GL85B
8-6	Perimeters and Areas of Squares	Cabri Jr.	GL86
Ch. 9	StudyCards Vocabulary/Concepts	StudyCards	GCH09MC, GCH09SC
Ch. 10	StudyCards Vocabulary/Concepts	StudyCards	GCH10MC, GCH10SC
Ch. 11	StudyCards Vocabulary/Concepts	StudyCards	GCH11MC, GCH11SC
11-3	Inscribed Angles	Cabri Jr.	GL113A, GL113B
Ch. 12	StudyCards Vocabulary/Concepts	StudyCards	GCH12MC, GCH12SC
12-1	Reflections	Cabri Jr.	———

Activities for *Algebra 2*

Chap/ Lesson	Activity	TI App(s)	Program(s)
Ch. 1	StudyCards Vocabulary/Concepts	StudyCards™	A2CH01MC, A2CH01SC
Ch. 2	StudyCards Vocabulary/Concepts	StudyCards	A2CH02MC, A2CH02SC
	Data Lists	———	A2CH02DL
2-2	Parallels and Perpendiculars	Transformation Graphing	A2L22
2-4	Visualizing Linear Models	Transformation Graphing	A2L24A, A2L24B, A2L24C
2-5	Absolute Value Translations I	Transformation Graphing	A2L25
2-6	Absolute Value Translations II	Transformation Graphing	A2L26
Ch. 3	StudyCards Vocabulary/Concepts	StudyCards	A2CH03MC, A2CH03SC
	Data Lists	———	A2CH03DL
3-3	General Inequality Systems	Inequality Graphing	A2L33A, A2L33B, A2L33C, A2L33D
3-4	Vertex Principle	Transformation Graphing	A2L34A
	Linear Programming	Inequality Graphing, Transformation Graphing	A2L34B, A2L34C
Ch. 4	StudyCards Vocabulary/Concepts	StudyCards	A2CH04MC, A2CH04SC
Ch. 5	StudyCards Vocabulary/Concepts	StudyCards	A2CH05MC, A2CH05SC
	Data Lists	———	A2CH05DL
5-2	Quadratic Translations I	Transformation Graphing	A2L52
5-3	Quadratic Translations II	Transformation Graphing	A2L53A
	Dodge 'Em	Transformation Graphing	A2L53B
	Quadratic Function Match II	Transformation Graphing	A2L53C
	Follow the Bouncing Ball I	Transformation Graphing	A2L53D
Ch. 6	StudyCards Vocabulary/Concepts	StudyCards	A2CH06MC, A2CH06SC
	Data Lists	———	A2CH06DL
6-2	Graphs, Zeros, and Factors	Transformation Graphing	A2L62A
	Polynomial Function Match	Transformation Graphing	A2L62B
Ch. 7	StudyCards Vocabulary/Concepts	StudyCards	A2CH07MC, A2CH07SC
7-8	Radical Translations I	Transformation Graphing	A2L78A
	Radical Translations II	Transformation Graphing	A2L78B
Ch. 8	StudyCards Vocabulary/Concepts	StudyCards	A2CH08MC, A2CH08SC
	Data Lists	———	A2CH08DL
8-1	Choose a Model II	Transformation Graphing	A2L81A
	Follow the Bouncing Ball II	Transformation Graphing	A2L81B
8-2	Asymptotes for Exponentials	Transformation Graphing	A2L82A, A2L82B
Ch. 9	StudyCards Vocabulary/Concepts	StudyCards	A2CH09MC, A2CH09SC
9-2	Asymptotes for Rationals	Transformation Graphing	A2L92
Ch. 10	StudyCards Vocabulary/Concepts	StudyCards	A2CH10MC, A2CH10SC
Ch. 11	StudyCards Vocabulary/Concepts	StudyCards	A2CH11MC, A2CH11SC
Ch. 12	StudyCards Vocabulary/Concepts	StudyCards	A2CH12MC, A2CH12SC
	Data Lists	———	A2CH12DL
Ch. 13	StudyCards Vocabulary/Concepts	StudyCards	A2CH13MC, A2CH13SC
	Data Lists	———	A2CH13DL
13-4	Sine Function Match	Transformation Graphing	A2L134
13-7	Cosine Function Match	Transformation Graphing	A2L137A
	Daylight Model	Transformation Graphing	A2L137B
Ch. 14	StudyCards Vocabulary/Concepts	StudyCards	A2CH14MC, A2CH14SC
	Data Lists	———	A2CH14DL

Correlation of Data Lists to Textbook Exercises

The *Algebra 1* and *Algebra 2* exercises listed below have data lists that students can process using a TI-83/84 Plus. These data lists are also on the CD under the file names shown. (Sometimes, you may see the file name preceded by a small ʟ; for example ʟEX4A. This tells the calculator that the name is for a list.) Transferring them—as groups or individually—will aid data-entry time and accuracy. You may wish to copy this correlation for students.

Key:

CQ: Checkpoint Quiz	EX: Example	MR: Mixed Review
CR: Chapter Review	Ex: Exercise (PRactice)	PR: Practice and Problem Solving
CT: Chapter Test	E EX: Extension Example	T EX: Technology Example
CU: Check Understanding	E Ex: Extension Exercise	T Ex: Technology Exercise
DK: Dorling Kindersley	EPR: Extension Exercise (PRactice)	TPR: Technology Exercise (PRactice)
DR: Diagnosing Readiness	INV St: Investigation Set	

Algebra 1

Ch/Les	Pg/Exercise	Group/List Names
Ch. 6		**A1CH06DL**
6-6	319 EX 2	EX2A, EX2B
6-6	320 CU 2	CU2A, CU2B
6-6	321 Ex 6	PR06A, PR06B
6-6	321 Ex 7	PR07A, PR07B
6-6	321 Ex 8	PR08A, PR08B
6-6	321 Ex 9	PR09A, PR09B
6-6	321 Ex 10	PR10A, PR10B
6-6	321 Ex 11	PR11A, PR11B
6-6	322 Ex 12	PR12A, PR12B
6-6	322 Ex 13	PR13A, PR13B
6-6	322 Ex 16	PR16A, PR16B
6-6	322 Ex 17	PR17A, PR17B
6-6	323 Ex 19b	PR19A, PR19B
6-6	323 Ex 20	PR20A, PR20B
6-6	324 CQ 9	CQ09A, CQ09B
6-6	324 CQ 10	CQ10A, CQ10B
6-7	329 MR 49	MR49A, MR49B
6-7	329 MR 50	MR50A, MR50B
CR	333 CR 34	CR34A, CR34B
CT	334 CT 36	CT36A, CT36B
CT	334 CT 37	CT37A, CT37B
Ch. 8		**A1CH08DL**
8-1	399 MR 97	MR97A, MR97B
8-7	436 T EX	TEXA, TEXB
8-7	436 T Ex 1	TPR1A, TPR1B
8-7	436 T Ex 2	TPR2A, TPR2B
8-7	436 T Ex 3	TPR3A, TPR3B
Ch. 9		**A1CH09DL**
9-7	495 MR 91	MR91A, MR91B
Ch. 10		**A1CH10DL**
10-9	564 Ex 17	PR17A, PR17B
10-9	564 Ex 19	PR19A, PR19B
10-9	564 Ex 20	PR20A, PR20B
10-9	564 Ex 21	PR21A, PR21B

Ch/Les	Pg/Exercise	Group/List Names
10-9	564 Ex 22	PR22A, PR22B
10-9	564 Ex 23	PR23A, PR23B
10-9	564 Ex 24	PR24A, PR24B
10-9	565 Ex 27	PR27A, PR27B
10-9	565 Ex 28	PR28A, PR28B
10-9	565 Ex 29	PR29A, PR29B

Algebra 2

Ch/Les	Pg/Exercise	Group/List Names
Ch. 2		**A2CH02DL**
2-4	80 EX 4	EX4A, EX4B
2-4	80 CU 4A	CU4AA, CU4AB
2-4	80 CU 4B	CU4BA, CU4BB
2-4	81 Ex 8	PR08A, PR08B
2-4	81 Ex 9	PR09A, PR09B
2-4	81 Ex 10	PR10A, PR10B
2-4	81 Ex 11	PR11A, PR11B
2-4	81 Ex 12	PR12A, PR12B
2-4	81 Ex 13	PR13A, PR13B
2-4	82 Ex 14	PR14A, PR14B, PR14C
2-4	82 Ex 20	PR20A, PR20B
2-4	83 Ex 21	PR21A, PR21B
2-4	83 Ex 27	PR27A, PR27B
2-4	83 Ex 28	PR28A, PR28B
2-4	85 T EX	TEXA, TEXB
2-4	85 T Ex 1	TPR1A, TPR1B
2-4	85 T Ex 2	TPR2A, TPR2B
2-4	85 T Ex 3	TPR3A, TPR3B
2-7	98 CQ 9	CQ09A, CQ09B
CR	108 CR 26	CR26A, CR26B
CR	109 CR 27	CR27A, CR27B
CR	109 CR 28	CR28A, CR28B
CT	110 CT 31	CT31A, CT31B
Ch. 3		**A2CH03DL**
3-1	117 EX 2	EX2A, EX2B, EX2C
3-1	119 Ex 10	PR10A, PR10B, PR10C

Data List Correlation (*Algebra 2*, continued)

Ch/Les	Pg/Exercise	**Group**/List Names	Ch/Les	Pg/Exercise	**Group**/List Names
3-1	119 Ex 11	PR11A, PR11B, PR11C	12-3	652 Ex 3	PR03
3-1	119 Ex 12	PR12A, PR12B, PR12C	12-3	652 Ex 4	PR04
3-4	140 MR 34	MR34A, MR34B	12-3	652 Ex 5	PR05
Ch. 5		**A2CH05DL**	12-3	652 Ex 6	PR06
DR	232 DR 13	DR13A, DR13B	12-3	652 Ex 7	PR07
DR	232 DR 14	DR14A, DR14B	12-3	653 Ex 13	PR13
5-1	236 EX 4	EX4A, EX4B	12-3	653 Ex 14	PR14
5-1	237 Ex 21	PR21A, PR21B	12-3	653 Ex 15	PR15
5-1	237 Ex 22	PR22A, PR22B	12-3	653 Ex 19	PR19
5-1	238 Ex 31	PR31A, PR31B	12-3	654 Ex 21	PR21A, PR21B
5-1	238 Ex 38	PR38A, PR38B	12-3	654 Ex 22	PR22A, PR22B, PR22C
5-1	240 T EX	TEXA, TEXB	12-3	655 CQ 8–9	CQ08, CQ09
5-1	240 T Ex 1	TPR1A, TPR1B	12-3	656 INV St 1	INV1
5-1	240 T Ex 2	TPR2A, TPR2B	12-3	656 INV St 2	INV2
5-3	253 Ex 57	PR57A, PR57B, PR57C	12-3	656 INV St 3	INV3
CR	294 CR 12	CR12A, CR12B	12-3	656 INV St 4	INV4
Ch. 6		**A2CH06DL**	12-4	658 EX 3	EX3
6-1	302 EX 2	EX2A, EX2B	12-4	659 CU 3	CU3
6-1	302 EX 3	EX3A, EX3B	12-4	660 Ex 4	PR04A
6-1	303 Ex 13	PR13A, PR13B	12-4	660 Ex 5	PR05A
6-1	303 Ex 14	PR14A, PR14B	12-4	660 Ex 6	PR06A
6-1	303 Ex 15	PR15A, PR15B	12-4	660 Ex 7	PR07A
6-1	303 Ex 16	PR16A, PR16B	12-4	661 Ex 15	PR15A, PR15B
6-1	303 Ex 17	PR17A, PR17B, PR17C	12-4	661 Ex 16	PR16A, PR16B
6-1	303 Ex 18	PR18A, PR18B	12-4	661 Ex 17	PR17A, PR17B
6-1	303 Ex 19	PR19A, PR19B	12-4	661 Ex 21	PR21
6-1	303 Ex 20	PR20A, PR20B	12-4	661 Ex 22	PR22
6-1	303 Ex 21	PR21A, PR21B	12-4	661 Ex 23	PR23
6-1	303 Ex 22	PR22A, PR22B	12-4	661 Ex 24	PR24
6-1	303 Ex 23	PR23A, PR23B	12-4	661 Ex 25	PR25
6-1	304 Ex 59	PR59A, PR59B	12-4	662 Ex 29	PR29A, PR29B
CR	353 CR 12	CR12A, CR12B	12-4	662 Ex 30	PR30A, PR30B
Ch. 8		**A2CH08DL**	12-4	662 Ex 35	MR35
8-1	429 Ex 59	PR59A, PR59B	12-4	662 Ex 36	MR36
8-1	430 T EX	TEXA, TEXB	12-5	669 MR 38	MR38
8-1	430 T Ex 1	TPR1A, TPR1B	12-5	669 MR 39	MR39
8-1	430 T Ex 2	TPR2A, TPR2B	12-6	677 CQ 1	CQ01
8-1	430 T Ex 3	TPR3A, TPR3B	12-6	677 CQ 2	CQ02
8-1	430 T Ex 4	TPR4A, TPR4B	12-6	677 CQ 3	CQ03
8-5	461 E EX	EEXA, EEXB	CR	688 CR 14	CR14
8-5	461 E Ex 1	EPR1A, EPR1B	CR	689 CR 20	CR20
8-5	461 E Ex 2	EPR2A, EPR2B	**Ch. 13**		**A2CH13DL**
8-6	466 Ex 65	PR65	13-6	740 MR 59	MR59
DK	475 DK Ex b	DKBA, DKBB	13-6	740 MR 60	MR60
Ch. 12		**A2CH12DL**	13-6	740 MR 61	MR61
12-3	649 EX 2	EX2	13-7	746 CU 6b	CU6A, CU6B
12-3	649 CU 2	CU2	13-7	747 Ex 44d	PR44A, PR44B
12-3	651 CU 4	CU4	**Ch. 14**		**A2CH14DL**
12-3	652 Ex 1	PR01	MR	768 MR 83	MR 83
12-3	652 Ex 2	PR02	MR	768 MR 84	MR 84

Topics in Algebra 1 Apps

Activities for Chapters 1–7 of the textbook *Algebra 1* are built into the
Topics in Algebra 1 Apps. Use the guide below to find the activities for the
TI-83/84 Plus. This guide will also help you locate the related worksheets and
Teacher Notes in the *Topics in Algebra 1* manuals on the CD.

Algebra 1 Lesson	App	Section(s)
1-3 Exploring Real Numbers	ALG1CH1 (Number Sense)	Integers, Rational Numbers, Real Numbers
1-4 Adding Real Numbers	ALG1CH1 (Number Sense)	Integers, Rational Numbers, Real Numbers
1-5 Subtracting Real Numbers	ALG1CH1 (Number Sense)	Integers, Rational Numbers, Real Numbers
1-6 Multiplying and Dividing Real Numbers	ALG1CH1 (Number Sense)	Integers, Rational Numbers, Real Numbers
1-7 The Distributive Property	ALG1CH1 (Number Sense)	Real Numbers
1-8 Properties of Real Numbers	ALG1CH1 (Number Sense)	Real Numbers
2-1 Solving One-Step Equations	ALG1CH2 (Linear Equations)	Using Graphs & Tables Using Algebra
2-2 Solving Two-Step Equations	ALG1CH2 (Linear Equations)	Using Algebra
3-1 Inequalities and Their Graphs	ALG1CH4 (Linear Inequalities)	Using Graphs & Tables
3-2 Solving Inequalities: Using Addition and Subtraction	ALG1CH4 (Linear Inequalities)	Using Graphs & Tables Using Algebra
3-3 Solving Inequalities: Using Multiplication and Division	ALG1CH4 (Linear Inequalities)	Using Algebra
5-2 Relations and Functions	ALG1CH2 (Linear Equations)	Using Graphs & Tables
5-3 Functions, Rules, Tables, and Graphs	ALG1CH2 (Linear Equations)	Using Graphs & Tables
6-1 Rate of Change and Slope	ALG1CH3 (Linear Functions)	Slope With Grid, Slope Using Coordinates, Slope as Rate of Change, Slope-Intercept Form
6-2 Slope-Intercept Form	ALG1CH3 (Linear Functions)	Slope-Intercept Form
7-1 Solving Systems by Graphing	ALG1CH5 (Linear Systems)	Using Graphs & Tables
7-2 Solving Systems Using Substitution	ALG1CH5 (Linear Systems)	Using Algebra
7-3 Solving Systems Using Elimination	ALG1CH5 (Linear Systems)	Using Algebra
7-4 Applications of Linear Systems	ALG1CH5 (Linear Systems)	Using Graphs & Tables Using Algebra

The Topics in Algebra 1 Apps have several built-in activities for Chapters 1–7 of the textbook *Algebra 1*. Each Activity is part of an accompanying worksheet with Teacher Notes in the *Topics in Algebra 1* manuals on the CD. Use the guide below to help you match activities with *Algebra 1* lessons.

Topics in Algebra 1 App	Activity	*Algebra 1* Lesson
ALG1CH1 (Number Sense)		
Integers	What Is My Sign?	1-3, 1-4, 1-5, 1-6
	Integer Smash	1-3, 1-4, 1-5, 1-6
Rational Numbers	Slide	Skills Handbook, pp. 724, 726
	Number Smash	1-3, 1-4, 1-5, 1-6, Skills Handbook, pp. 724–726
Real Numbers	Raining Reals	1-3
	What Is My Property?	1-7, 1-8
ALG1CH2 (Linear Equations)		
Using Graphs & Tables	Beam Dale Up	2-1
	Worksheet Activity	5-2, 5-3
Using Algebra	Solve It!	2-1, 2-2
	Beam Dale Up	2-1, 2-2
	Free Fall	2-1, 2-2
ALG1CH3 (Linear Functions)		
Slope With Grid	Screen Cross	6-1
	Linked Calculators Screen Cross	6-1
	Draw the Slopes!	6-1
Slope Using Coordinates	Screen Cross	6-1
	Linked Calculators Screen Cross	6-1
Slope as Rate of Change	Balloon Speed	6-1
	Dive	6-1
Slope-Intercept Form	Match It!	6-2
	Line Soccer	6-2
ALG1CH4 (Linear Inequalities)		
Using Graphs & Tables	Build the Solution Set!	3-1
	Worksheet Activity 1	3-1
	Worksheet Activity 2	3-1
Using Algebra	Solve It!	3-2, 3-3
	Free Fall	3-2, 3-3
ALG1CH5 (Linear Systems)		
Using Graphs & Tables	System Match It!	7-1
	Worksheet Activity	7-1, 7-4
Using Algebra	What Am I?	7-2, 7-3, 7-4
	Balloon Ride	7-2, 7-3, 7-4

Measurement Conversions

For Use With Lesson 5-5

FILES NEEDED: Science Tools App

In the Science Tools App, you can use the UNIT CONVERTER to switch from one unit to another. Follow this example to convert 2 meters to feet.

In the UNIT CONVERTER, find and open the LENGTH menu.

```
    SELECT A TOOL
1: SIG-FIG CALCULATOR
2: UNIT CONVERTER
3: DATA/GRAPHS WIZARD
4: VECTOR CALCULATOR


[EXIT]
```

```
    UNIT CONVERTER
1: LENGTH    7: MASS
2: AREA      8: FORCE/WT
3: VOLUME    9: PRESSURE
4: TIME      A: ENERGY/WORK
5: TEMP      B: POWER
6: VELOCITY  C: SI PREFIXES
[CONSTANT]
```

Type 2, the number of meters you want to convert.

Choose the given unit of measure and press ENTER.

Choose the desired unit of measure and press ENTER.

```
         LENGTH
 fm    A    mm   cm   m
 km   Mil   in   ft   yd
 fath  rd   mi   nmi  ltyr
 2
[CONSTANT][EXPT][COPY][EDIT]
```

```
         LENGTH
 fm    A    mm   cm   m
 km   Mil   in   ft   yd
 fath  rd   mi   nmi  ltyr
 2E0 m▸
[CONSTANT][EXPT][COPY][EDIT]
```

```
         LENGTH
 fm    A    mm   cm   m
 km   Mil   in   ft   yd
 fath  rd   mi   nmi  ltyr
 2E0 m▸
       6.5616E0 ft
[CONSTANT][EXPT][COPY][EDIT]
```

The screen shows 2 m ≈ 6.56 ft.

1. The converted value appears in a calculator form of scientific notation. Write the standard form for each number given in calculator scientific notation below. (If scientific notation is new to you, look ahead to Lesson 8-2.)

   a. 1.23E1   b. 1.23E–1   c. 4.56E2   d. 4.56E–2

2. Use the UNIT CONVERTER to complete the table. State whether the converted values vary directly with the given measurements. If they do, write an equation for the direct variation.

   a. Length

meters	feet
2	6.56
3	
4	
6	

   b. Volume

liters	gallons
2	
3	
4	
6	1.59

   c. Temperature

°C	°F
2	
3	
4	
6	

   d. Volume

cups	gallons
2	
3	
4	
6	

Measurement Conversions

Activity Objective

Students use the Science Tools App to convert measurements.

Correlation to Text

- Lesson 5-5: Direct Variation

Time

- 15–20 minutes

Materials/Software

- App: Science Tools
- Activity worksheet

Classroom Management

- Students can work individually or in pairs depending on the number of calculators available.

Notes

- Students may need to review scientific notation, or study it in Lesson 8-2 before answering Question 1.

Answers

1. **a.** 12.3   **b.** 0.123   **c.** 456   **d.** 0.0456

2. **a.** Length; $y = 3.28x$

meters	feet
2	6.56
3	9.84
4	13.12
6	19.69

b. Volume; $y = 0.265x$

liters	gallons
2	0.53
3	0.79
4	1.06
6	1.59

c. Temperature; not direct variation

°C	°F
2	35.6
3	37.4
4	39.2
6	42.8

d. Volume; $y = 0.0625x$

cups	gallons
2	0.13
3	0.19
4	0.25
6	0.38

Linear Graphs

For Use With Lesson 6-2

FILES NEEDED: Transformation Graphing App
Program: **A1L62A**

A1L62A shows the linear equation or function
$y = mx + b$ graphed as Y1 = AX + B.

In this activity, you will explore the graph of
$y = mx + b$.

1. Run **A1L62A**. Increment the values of **A** in steps of 1. How does the graph change?

2. Predict how the graph will change when you increment the values of **A** in steps of −1. Test your prediction.

3. Increment the values of **B** in steps of 1. How does the graph change?

4. Predict how the graph will change when you increment the values of **B** in steps of −1. Test your prediction.

5. Set **A** = 0 and **B** = 5. What kind of line do you see?

6. Predict what will happen for **A** = 5 and **B** = 0. Test your prediction.

Extension

7. Is it possible to make the line vertical by adjusting the values of A and B? Explain.

8. If **A1L62A** had set up the graph of Y1 = A + BX instead of Y1 = AX + B, how would the results for the activities above differ? Explain.

Animation Option

Set the Transformation Graphing App and select
Play [>] as shown at the right. Set **A** = −3, **B** = 1,
Step = 1, and **Max** = 5. Select A for incrementing.

9. Press GRAPH and watch the values of **A** increase from −3 to 5. Does the line move the same amount with each change? Explain.

10. Select B for incrementing. Before you press GRAPH, predict what you will see.
Press GRAPH and check your prediction.

Linear Graphs

Activity Objective

Students use the Transformation Graphing App to explore the graph of the function $y = mx + b$.

Correlation to Text

- Lesson 6-2: Slope-Intercept Form

Time

- 15–20 minutes

Materials/Software

- Transformation Graphing App
- Program: **A1L62A**
- Activity worksheet

Skills Needed

- start an App

Classroom Management

- Students can work individually or in pairs depending on the number of calculators available.
- Use TI Connect™ software, TI-GRAPH LINK™ software, the TI-Navigator™ system, or unit-to-unit links to transfer **A1L62A** to each calculator.

Notes

- Remind students that **Y1 = AX + B** is screen notation for $y = mx + b$, where **A** $= m$.
- Some values in the Play **SETTINGS** may lead to errors. The number of screens is determined by how many times the selected value can be incremented without exceeding the **Max** value.

Answers

1. The line tilts upward to the right.

2. The line will tilt downward to the right.

3. The line moves up but its tilt doesn't change.

4. The line will move down.

5. a horizontal line through $(0, 5)$

6. a steep line through $(0, 0)$

7. No; as the value of **A** get larger and larger, the line gets closer to vertical but will not reach it.

8. The answers for Questions 1–6 would be the answers above for Questions 3, 4, 1, 2, 6, 5, respectively. The answer for 7 would be the answer above for 7 with **A** replaced by **B**.

9. No; the line moves the most when **A** changes from -1 to 0 and from 0 to -1.

10. The line will move up.

Linear Function Match

For Use With Lesson 6-2

> **FILES NEEDED:** Transformation Graphing App, Guess My Coefficients App
> Program: A1L62B

A1L62B graphs the linear equation or function $y = mx + b$ as Y1 = AX + B
with A = 0 and B = 6.

In this activity you will see three scatter plots, one at a time. You are
to change the A and B values for Y1 = AX + B until you find a
function $y = mx + b$ that is a perfect match
for the given plot.

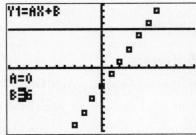

1. Run the Transformation Graphing App and
   A1L62B. Find a linear function whose graph
   matches the plot.

2. Switch from Plot1 to Plot2. Press **GRAPH** to see A1L62B for the
   second plot. Find a matching linear function.

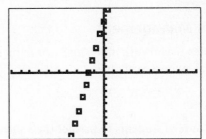

3. Switch from Plot2 to Plot3. Press **GRAPH**
   to see A1L62B for the third plot. Find a
   matching linear function.

4. Run the Guess My Coefficients (**GuesCoef**) App.
   Play the $y = mx + b$ version of the LINEAR game.

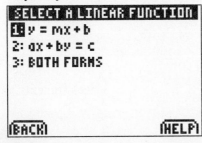

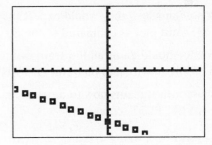

Extension

Use Plot1 in the Transformation Graphing App. For each equation below, replace
data lists L1 and L2 with three ordered pairs that are solutions of the equation.
Then find a linear function $y = mx + b$ whose graph contains the three points.

5. $2x + 3y = 6$ 6. $4x - 2y = 4$ 7. $x + 3y = 9$

Linear Function Match

Activity Objective

Students use the Transformation Graphing App to learn how changing the values of m and b affects the graph of $y = mx + b$.

Correlation to Text

- Lesson 6-2: Slope-Intercept Form

Time

- 10–15 minutes

Materials/Software

- Transformation Graphing App, Guess My Coefficients App
- Program: A1L62B   • Activity worksheet

Skills Needed

- change parameter values

Classroom Management

- Students can work individually or in pairs depending on the number of calculators available.

Notes

- Encourage students to predict the values of A and B before trying to match each plot.
- Ask students how they would expect the value of A to be different for the third plot as compared to the first two plots.
- Students should uninstall the Transformation Graphing App at the end of this activity, and then run DEFAULT to reset their calculators.
- Discuss with students how to deselect and select a plot in either the Y= or STAT PLOT screens.

Answers

1. $y = 2x - 3$ **2.** $y = 5x + 8$ **3.** $y = -0.5x - 8$ **4.** Check students' work.

5–7. Ordered pairs may vary: Samples are given.

5. $(0, 2), (3, 0), (6, -2); y = -0.67x + 2$, or $y = -\frac{2}{3}x + 2$

6. $(0, -2), (1, 0), (2, 2); y = 2x - 2$

7. $(0, 3), (9, 0), (3, 2); y = -0.33x + 3$, or $y = -\frac{1}{3}x + 3$

Line 'Em Up

For Use With Lesson 6-2

> **FILES NEEDED:** Transformation Graphing App
> Program: **A1L62C**

The **A1L62C** startup screen shows 14 points plotted in Quadrant I.
It also shows the graph of a linear function in the form Y1 = AX + B
with A = 1 and B = −1.

In this activity you are to change the values of A and
B to find equations for the lines described. Write the
equation of each line you find.

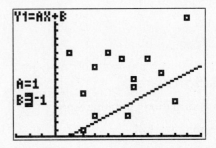

1. Run A1L62C. Write the equation of the line
   shown on the screen. It passes through one
   of the plotted points. What are the
   coordinates of that point? Check that
   it is a solution of your equation.

2. Change the values of A and B and find a line that passes through
   two points. Make a guess as to how many such lines you could find.

3. Find a line that passes through three plotted points. Can you find any
   that pass through four plotted points?

4. Find horizontal lines that pass through at least two points each.

5. Find vertical lines that pass through at least two points each.
   (*Hint:* You cannot do this by changing the values of A and B.)

6. Can you find a line with positive slope that has on each side of it
   approximately one half of the points that it doesn't pass through?
   Can you find a line with negative slope that separates the points in
   the same way?

Extension

7. If no three of the 14 points were to be collinear, about how many different
   equations would have graphs passing through two of the 14 points?
   (Compare your answer with your guess in Question 2.)

8. If there would be only one set of three collinear points among the 14 given
   points, then how many different equations would have graphs passing
   through at least two points each?

9. If there was exactly one set of four collinear points and only one (different)
   set of three collinear points, then how many different equations would have
   graphs passing through at least two points each?

Line 'Em Up

Activity Objective

Students use the Transformation Graphing App to learn how changing the values of m and b affects the graph of $y = mx + b$.

Correlation to Text

- Lesson 6-2: Slope-Intercept Form

Time

- 20–25 minutes

Materials/Software

- Transformation Graphing App
- Program: A1L62C
- Activity worksheet

Skills Needed

- change parameter values

Classroom Management

- Students can work individually or in pairs depending on the number of calculators available.

Notes

- Sometimes a line will darken the interior of a point mark. Point out that a dark interior does not necessarily mean the point is on the line, nor does a light interior mean that a point is not on a line.
- Students can use `TRACE` to find the coordinates of a plotted point or a point on a line.

Answers

1. $y = x - 1; (2, 1)$

2.   Answers may vary. (See Question 7.)

3.   Answers may vary. Sample: The graph for $y = -x + 13$ passes through three plotted points. No line passes through four plotted points.

4. $y = 3, y = 11, y = 12$

5. $x = 2, x = 3, x = 6$

6.   Check students' work.

7.   91 equations   8.   89 equations   9.   84 equations

Writing Equations of Lines

For Use With Lesson 6-4

FILES NEEDED: Guess My Coefficients App

In this activity you practice writing equations of lines in both slope-intercept form $y = mx + b$ and standard form $ax + by = c$.

Write a description of the graph of each equation.

1. $y = 3x + 5$ **2.** $y = -2x - 1$ **3.** $y = 7$ **4.** $x = -2$

Write an equation for each graph shown below. Use $y = mx + b$ form. The scale on each axis is marked in unit intervals.

5.
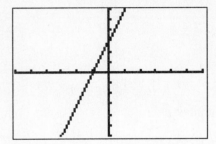

6.
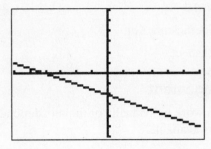

Find the x- and y-intercepts for each line given below. On graph paper, use the intercepts to locate two points of the graph. Then draw the graph.

7. $2x + 3y = 6$ **8.** $x - 2y = 4$ **9.** $4x + 2y = 4$ **10.** $-2x - 3y = 6$

Write an equation for each graph given below. Use $ax + by = c$ form.

11.
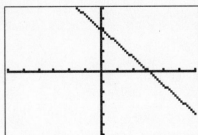

12.
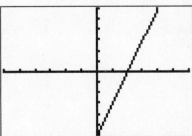

13. For more practice, run the Guess My Coefficients (**GuesCoef**) App. Play the BOTH FORMS version of the LINEAR game.

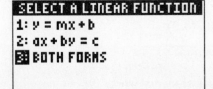

Writing Equations of Lines

Activity Objective

Students use the Guess My Coefficients App to practice writing equations of lines in slope-intercept form, $y = mx + b$, and standard form, $ax + by = c$.

Correlation to Text

- Lesson 6-4: Point-Slope Form and Writing Linear Equations

Time

- 15–25 minutes

Materials/Software

- Guess My Coefficients App
- Activity worksheet

Classroom Management

- Students can work individually or in pairs depending on the number of calculators available.

Notes

- Students can review Lesson 6-3 if they need help with standard form.

Answers

1–4. Answers may vary. Samples are given.

1. a line with slope 3 and y-intercept 5

2. a line with slope –2 and y-intercept –1

3. a horizontal line through $(0, 7)$

4. a vertical line through $(-2, 0)$

5. $y = 3x + 3$

6. $y = -\frac{1}{2}x - 2$

7-10. Check that students' graphs have the correct intercepts.

7. $(3, 0), (0, 2)$

8. $(4, 0), (0, -2)$

9. $(1, 0), (0, 2)$

10. $(-3, 0), (0, -2)$

11. $4x + 3y = 12$

12. $6x - 2y = 12$

13. Check students' work.

Name_____ Class_____ Date_____

Trend Lines

FILES NEEDED: Transformation Graphing App
                Programs: A1L66A, A1L66B, A1L66C

Each program for this activity graphs the linear
equation $y = mx + b$ as $Y1 = AX + B$.

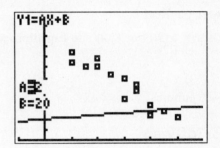

In this activity, you will use $y = mx + b$ to explore
trend lines.

If a scatter plot suggests a relationship between two
data sets, a *trend line* provides a mathematical model
for the relationship. For a line to be a trend line, you
want the points of the scatter plot to cluster around
the line and the points of the line to approximate
the points of the scatter plot.

Each program for this activity relates to an exercise in Lesson 6-6 of your
textbook, pages 320–321. Run the program. Manipulate the line shown in the
window to make the best trend line you can. Write the equation of the line.
Then answer the related question(s).

1. Program A1L66A
   (Exercise 4)

   The scatter plot compares study time x to response speed y in a
   memory test. Use your trend line. What is an estimated response
   speed for a study time of 5.5 minutes?

2. Program A1L66B
   (Exercise 7)

   The scatter plot compares latitude (°N) with average temperature
   (°F). Does your trend line have positive slope or negative slope?
   What does the sign of the slope tell you about the relationship
   between latitude and temperature? At what latitude would you
   expect to find an average temperature of 45°F?

3. Program A1L66C
   (Exercise 11)

   The scatter plot compares air temperature and wind-chill
   temperature when the wind speed is 15 mi/h. Use your trend
   line. Estimate the wind-chill temperature when the air temperature
   is 23°F.

Extension

Work with another student. Compare your trend lines.

4. For the memory test (Question 1 above), explain any differences you
   find in your trend lines. Compare your explanations.

5. You will likely find that your wind-chill-temperature trend lines
   (Question 3) are more alike than those for the memory test and the
   temperatures in northern latitudes. Why might this be so?

Trend Lines

Activity Objective

Students use the Transformation Graphing App to make trend lines.

Correlation to Text

- Lesson 6-6: Scatter Plots and Equations of Lines

Time

- 15–20 minutes

Materials/Software

- Transformation Graphing App
- Programs: A1L66A, A1L66B, and A1L66C
- Activity worksheet

Skills Needed

- start an App
- change parameter values

Classroom Management

- Students can work individually or in pairs depending on the number of calculators available.
- Use TI Connect™ software, TI-GRAPH LINK™ software, the TI-Navigator™ system, or unit-to-unit links to transfer A1L66A, A1L66B, and A1L66C to each calculator.

Notes

- Complete this Activity before students study Example 2 on page 319.
- When the equal sign next to the parameter is highlighted, students can change parameters A or B by entering the values directly.
- Use value in the CALC menu to find a y-value for a given x-value on the trend line.

Answers

Answer may vary. Samples are given.

1. $y = -16x + 98$; 10 s

2. $y = -0.9x + 87$; negative; As the latitude increases, the average temperature decreases. $\approx 46°N$

3. $y = 1.5x - 34$; $0.5°F$ 4. Check students' work.   5. The data are very close to being linear.

Absolute Value Graphs

FILES NEEDED: Transformation Graphing App
Program: **A1L67**

This activity uses the Transformation Graphing App to model bank shots on a pool table. A bank shot bounces off a cushion (the inner rim of the pool table top) at the same angle that it approaches the cushion.

Rules and Scoring

In **A1L67**, the 11 plotted points represent pool balls. The graph is that of an absolute value equation of the form **Y1 = A abs(X – B) + C**.

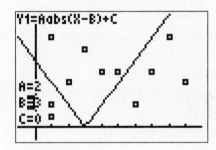

Your task is to find values for **A**, **B**, and **C** so that the graph strikes the pool balls. You can hit a pool ball with any part of the graph. The vertex of the graph must sit on the *x*-axis in the first quadrant.

Score one point for each ball struck.

EXAMPLE: The score for the startup graph in **A1L67** is 0 because the graph hits no pool balls.

OBJECT: Find values for **A**, **B**, and **C** to score the greatest number of points.

1.   Do the rules limit the values of **C** you can use? Explain.

2.   How does changing the value of **A** affect the shape of the graph?

3.   How does the object of the game limit the values of **A** you can use?

4.   How does changing the value of **B** affect the graph?

5.   Finding a graph whose score is 1 is easy. Why?

6.   Finding a graph whose score is 2 is easy. Why?

7.   For what scores greater than 2 can you find a graph? Write the equation for your highest-scoring graph. What is its score?

Extension

8.   Explain how to modify the game so that the graph uses the top of the screen as the cushion for its bank shots.

9.   Explain why it would be difficult to use the left or right side of the screen as the cushion.

Absolute Value Graphs

Activity Objective

Students use the Transformation Graphing App to explore absolute value graphs.

Correlation to Text

- Lesson 6-7: Graphing Absolute Value Equations

Time

- 30–45 minutes

Materials/Software

- Transformation Graphing App
- Program: **A1L67**
- Activity worksheet

Skills Needed

- change parameter values

Classroom Management

- Students can work individually or in pairs depending on the number of calculators available.
- Use TI Connect™ software, TI-GRAPH LINK™ software, the TI-Navigator™ system, or unit-to-unit links to transfer **A1L67** to each calculator.

Notes

- The text discusses the forms $y = |x| + k$ and $y = |x - h|$, but does not deal directly with $y = a|x - h| + k$.
- Investigating the parameters **A**, **B**, and **C** separately may be helpful for students who have trouble seeing how each parameter affects the graph.

Answers

1. Because the vertex must be on the x-axis, the minimum value must be $y = 0$, so **C** must equal 0.

2. The value of **A** affects how narrow or wide the V-shape is.

3. To hit any points, **A** must by greater than zero.

4. Changing **B** translates the graph to the left or right.

5. There are infinitely many lines through any point.

6. Two points determine a line. You can pass a branch of the graph through any two points.

7. Check students' work.   8. Let **C** = 11. Use negative values for **A**.

9. Y1 gives the graph of a function. A function does not have two points of its graph in line vertically.

Tortoise and the Hare

For Use With Lesson 7-1

> **FILES NEEDED:** Transformation Graphing App
> Program: A1L71

The diagram at the right models the race of the tortoise and the hare, described on page 344 of your textbook. To understand the model you have to first answer Questions 1 and 2 correctly. Their answers are shown upside down at the bottom of this page.

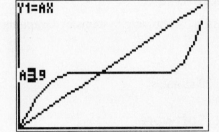

1. Run A1L71. Which graph belongs to each animal? Explain.

2. The horizontal axis represents time. Does the vertical axis represent distance or speed? Explain.

3. For the correct answer to Question 2, explain what each graph shows. Also, for the diagram above, explain what the top of the screen represents and how the diagram shows that the turtle won the race.

The distance run by the turtle is modeled by the equation $y = ax$, graphed above as Y1 = AX. You can vary the slope, a, of the line and determine values of a for which the turtle would win, lose, or tie.

When you use your calculator for the remaining questions, change A values by 0.1. You should enter directly each new value that you want to view.

4. For what values of A will the tortoise win the race?

5. For what values of A will the tortoise lose the race?

6. For what value of A will the tortoise and the hare tie in the race?

7. For what values of A will the tortoise not only lose the race but never be ahead of the hare?

8. For approximately what value of A will the tortoise pass the hare just as soon as the hare stops to take a rest?

9. For what values of A will the tortoise be ahead for part of the race but still lose?

10. For the model, what does a represent? How does a relate to the moral of the fable, "Slow and steady wins the race"?

11. On the diagram above, draw an interval along the time axis over which you think the turtle was running faster than the hare. Explain your drawing.

2. Distance; if the vertical axis showed speed, the turtle's graph would be a horizontal line.

The graph that's a line belongs to the tortoise.

1. The hare took a nap during the race. The flat part belongs to the hare.

Tortoise and the Hare

Activity Objective

Students use the Transformation Graphing App to interpret slopes and graphs.

Correlation to Text

- Lesson 7-1: Solving Systems by Graphing

Time

- 15–20 minutes

Materials/Software

- Transformation Graphing App
- Program: A1L71
- Activity worksheet

Classroom Management

- Students can work individually or in pairs depending on the number of calculators available.
- Use TI Connect™ software, TI-GRAPH LINK™ software, the TI-Navigator™ system, or unit-to-unit links to transfer **A1L71** to each calculator.

Notes

- Discuss with the class the correct interpretation of the graphs, including where the finish line is located on the screen.
- Remind students that they can enter values directly into **A=**. Type the value; then press ENTER .
- Remind students to uninstall the Transformation Graphing App when they complete the activity, and then run **DEFAULT**.

Answers

3. The line shows the tortoise's steady progress. The other graph shows the hare running quickly, covering distance faster than the tortoise, but then slowing down and coming to a stop for a nap. The tortoise passes the hare at the point of intersection. Later the hare starts moving again very fast, but the tortoise reaches the finish line (the top of the screen) first.

4. $A \geq 0.9$

5. $A \leq 0.8$

6. some value between 0.8 and 0.9

7. $A < 0.5$

8. $A \approx 1.5$

9. $0.5 < A < 0.8$

10. The tortoise's speed; the tortoise maintained a steady speed.

11. Check students' work; the interval along which the slope of the hare's graph is less than the slope of the tortoise's graph.

Name_____ Class_____ Date_____

Linear Systems I

FILES NEEDED: Transformation Graphing App
Program: **A1L72A**

You run two battery-powered cars in opposite directions across the classroom floor. You use a motion detector to plot the distance/time graphs shown here.

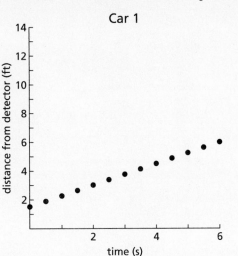

Car 1

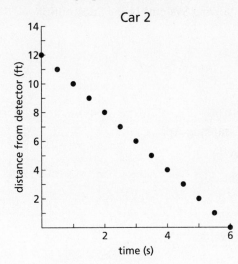

Car 2

1. One car moved away from the motion detector. The other moved toward it. Which car moved away from the motion detector?

2. About how far from the motion detector did each car start?

3. If both cars started at the same time, when did they pass each other?

4. When they passed, how far was each from the motion detector?

5. Which car moved faster? Explain.

6. Run **A1L72A** to see the plot for Car 1. The screen also shows the line $y = mx + b$ graphed as **Y1 = AX + B** with A = 0 and B = 6. Change the values of A and B to find a reasonable model for the distance/ time plot of Car 1. Find values for A and B to 2 decimal places. Write your model in the form $y = mx + b$.

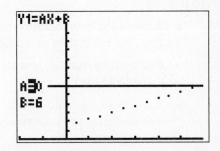

7. Switch from **Plot1** to **Plot2**. Press GRAPH to see **A1L72A** for Car 2. Use the procedure from Question 6 and find a model for the distance/time plot of Car 2.

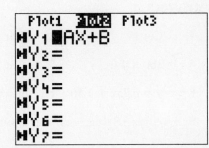

8. Use your models from Questions 6 and 7 and a method of your choice to answer Questions 3 and 4. Check the reasonableness of your answers with the plots at the top of this page.

Linear Systems I

Activity Objective

Students use the Transformation Graphing App to interpret graphs and the point of intersection of two lines.

Correlation to Text

- after Lesson 7-2: Solving Systems Using Substitution

Time

- 10–15 minutes

Materials/Software

- Transformation Graphing App
- Program: A1L72A
- Activity worksheet

Skills Needed

- change parameter values
- select and deselect a plot

Classroom Management

- Students can work individually or in pairs depending on the number of calculators available.
- Use TI Connect™ software, TI-GRAPH LINK™ software, the TI-Navigator™ system, or unit-to-unit links to transfer A1L72A to each calculator.

Notes

- Remind students that they can enter values directly into A= or B=. Type the value; then press ENTER .
- Discuss with students how to deselect and select a plot in either the Y= or STAT PLOT screens.
- Students should uninstall the Transformation Graphing App when they complete the activity, and then run DEFAULT.

Answers

1. Car 1
2. Car 1: ≈1.5 ft; Car 2: 12 ft
3. about 4 s
4. about 4 ft
5. Car 2; It traveled 12 ft in 6 s, while car 1 traveled about 4.5 ft in 6 s.
6. $y = 0.75x + 1.50$
7. $y = -2x + 12$
8. After 3.8 s each car was about 4.4 ft from the detector.

Name_____ Class_____ Date_____

Linear Systems II

FILES NEEDED: Transformation Graphing App
Program: A1L72B

You race two battery-powered cars in the same direction across the classroom floor. You use a motion detector to plot the distance/time graphs shown here.

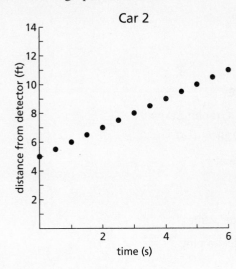

1. About how far from the motion detector did each car start?

2. How much of a head start did you give Car 2?

3. Which car moved faster? Explain.

4. If both cars started at the same time and the race lasted exactly 6 s as shown in the plots, did Car 1 catch Car 2? If so, how far were the cars from the motion detector?

5. Run A1L72B to see the plot for Car 1. The screen also shows the line $y = mx + b$ graphed as Y1 = AX + B with A = 0 and B = 6. Change the values of A and B to find a reasonable model for the distance/time plot of Car 1. Write your model in the form $y = mx + b$.

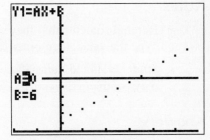

6. Switch from Plot1 to Plot2. Press **GRAPH** to see A1L72B for Car 2. Use the procedure from Question 5 and find a model for the distance/time plot of Car 2.

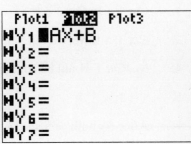

7. Use your models from Questions 5 and 6 and a method of your choice to find when and where Car 1 catches Car 2. Check the reasonableness of your answers with the plots above.

8. If the race lasted 10 s, which car would be farther from the motion detector? How much farther?

Linear Systems II

Activity Objective

Students use the Transformation Graphing App to develop interpretations of linear data.

Correlation to Text

- after Lesson 7-2: Solving Systems Using Substitution

Time

- 10–15 minutes

Materials/Software

- Transformation Graphing App
- Programs: A1L72B
- Activity worksheet

Skills Needed

- change parameter values
- select and deselect a plot

Classroom Management

- Students can work individually or in pairs depending on the number of calculators available.
- Use TI Connect™ software, TI-GRAPH LINK™ software, the TI-Navigator™ system, or unit-to-unit links to transfer A1L72B to each calculator.

Notes

- Remind students that they can enter values directly into A= or B=. Type the value; then press ENTER .
- Students should uninstall the Transformation Graphing App when they complete the activity, and then run DEFAULT.

Answers

1. Car 1: 1 ft; Car 2: 5 ft
2. 4 feet
3. Car 1; it travels about 9 ft in the same time that Car 2 travels about 6 ft.
4. No, Car 1 would be 10 ft away while Car 2 would be 11 ft away.
5. $y = 1.5x + 1$
6. $y = x + 5$
7. After 8 s both cars are 13 ft from the motion detector.
8. Car 1; 1 ft

Linear Inequality Graphs .... **For Use With Lesson 7-5**

FILES NEEDED: Inequality Graphing App

In this activity you practice graphing linear inequalities. After you graph each inequality by hand, use the Inequality Graphing App to check your work.

Follow this example to graph $y > x + 1$ using the Inequality Graphing App Inequal.

In the Y1= line of the Y= screen, select "=." In the list of inequality signs at the screen bottom, note that ">" is above F4. Press **ALPHA** F4.

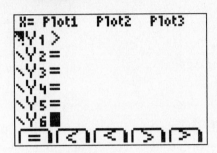

Enter Y1 > X + 1 and . . .

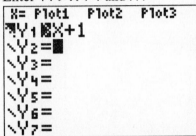

press **GRAPH** .

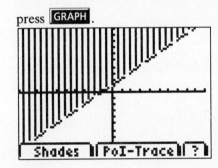

On graph paper, graph each inequality given below. Then use the Inequality Graphing App to draw each graph. Compare graphs. Describe how the screen graph distinguishes a "<" boundary line from a "≤" boundary line.

   1. $y < 2x + 5$ **2.** $y \le 7 - 3x$ **3.** $y \ge 3x - 6$ **4.** $6x + 2y > 10$

Extension

   5.   Use the Inequality Graphing App to graph
       Y1 ≤ −3X + 4 and Y2 > 5X − 2 on one
       screen. Press **ALPHA** F2 and experiment with
       the SHADES menu.

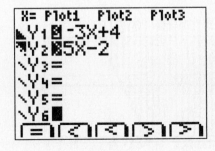

Linear Inequality Graphs

Activity Objective

Students use the Inequality Graphing App to practice graphing
linear inequalities.

Correlation to Text

- Lesson 7-5: Linear Inequalities

Time

- 15–25 minutes

Materials/Software

- Inequality Graphing App
- Activity worksheet

Classroom Management

- Students can work individually or in pairs depending on the number
  of calculators available.

Notes

- Before using the Inequality Graphing App to draw each graph, students
  may wish to run DEFAULT to reset the App to its default values.

Answers

1–4. Answers may vary. Sample: A "<" boundary line shows distinct gaps compared to a "≤" boundary line.

1.
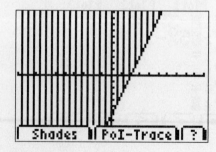

2.
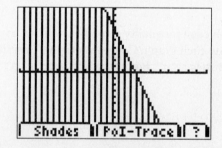

3.

4.
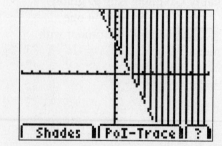

5. Check students' work.

Name _____ Class _____ Date _____

Linear Inequality Systems

FILES NEEDED: Inequality Graphing App
　　　　　　　　Program: **A1L76**

The graphs of two linear inequalities whose boundary lines intersect in one
point form four regions in the plane. In this activity you study those four regions.

1.　Run A1L76. The screen (below left) shows the graphs of $y = -0.5x + 2$
　　and $y = 2x - 2$. Which graph belongs to which equation? Explain.

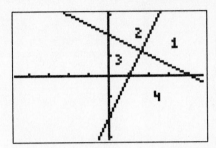　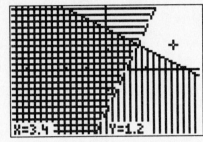

2.　Use the Inequality Graphing App. Graph **Y1 ≤ −0.5X + 2** and
　　Y2 > 2X − 2 on one screen (above right). Use the cursor to locate two
　　points in each of the four regions of the plane. Record the coordinates
　　in a table like the one below. Complete each line of the table before
　　you locate a new point. You should fill out eight table lines in all.

Region	Number of shadings	Point	Substitute in $y \le -0.5x + 2$.	Solution?	Substitute in $y > 2x - 2$.	Solution?
1	0	(3.4, 1.2)	$1.2 \le -0.5(3.4) + 2$ $1.2 \le 0.3$	no	$1.2 \ge 2(3.4) - 2$ $1.2 \ge 4.8$	no
1						
2						
2						
3						

3.　Generalize: Where a point satisfies two inequalities, the graph has __?__ shading(s).
　　Where a point satisfies only one inequality, the graph has __?__ shading(s).
　　Where a point satisfies neither inequality, the graph has __?__ shading(s).

Write a system of inequalities for each graph. Check your answer by
entering your inequalities as **Y1** and **Y2**.

4.
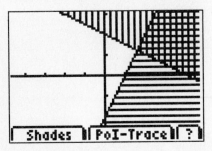

5.
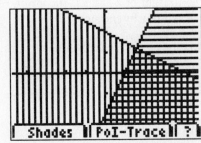

Linear Inequality Systems

Activity Objective

Students use the Inequality Graphing App to graph systems of two linear inequalities and to understand the four regions of the plane that result when the boundary lines intersect in one point.

Correlation to Text

- Lesson 7-6: Systems of Linear Inequalities

Time

- 20–25 minutes

Materials/Software

- Inequality Graphing App
- Program: A1L76
- Activity worksheet

Skills Needed

- insert inequality sign

Classroom Management

- Students can work individually or in pairs depending on the number of calculators available.

Error Prevention

- Remind students that the "1", "2", "3", and "4" in the startup screen correspond to the shaded regions and not to the quadrants.

Notes

- Use TI Connect™ software, TI-GRAPH LINK™ software, the TI-Navigator™ system, or unit-to-unit links to transfer A1L76 to each calculator.

Answers

1. The line below 1 and 2 is the graph of $y = -0.5x + 2$.
   The line to right of 2 and 3 is the graph of $y = 2x - 2$.
   You can tell this by the slopes.

2. Answers may vary. Check students' work.

3. 2; 1; 0

4. $y \geq -0.5x + 2$; $y \leq 2x - 2$

5. $y \leq -0.5x + 2$; $y \leq 2x - 2$

Exponential Graphs

For Use With Lesson 8-7

> **FILES NEEDED:** Transformation Graphing App
> Program: A1L87

A1L87 graphs the exponential function $y = ab^x$ as Y1 = AB^X.

In this activity, you will explore the graph of $y = ab^x$.

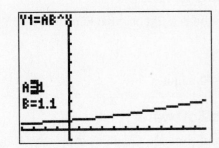

1. Run A1L87. Increment the value of A in steps of 1. (See Animation Option below.) What happens to the graph as A increases?

2. Reset the value of A to 1. Select B and enter values 1.5, 1.75, 2, and 3. What happens to the graph as B increases?

3. Does y have a maximum value when A > 0 and B > 1?

4. Set A = 8 and B = 1. Describe the graph. Explain why the graph makes sense.

5. Select B and enter values 1, 0.8, 0.6, 0.4, and 0.2. What happens to the graph in Quadrant I as B decreases, 0 < B < 1?

6. Fill in the chart. Summarize what you have learned about the effect of B for A > 0.

Describe the graph when B = 1.	
Describe the graph when 0 < B < 1.	
Describe the graph when B > 1.	
What happens to the graph when B increases from 1?	
What happens to the graph when B decreases from 1 (B > 0)?	

Extension

7. For A > 0 and 0 < B < 1, what happens to Y as X gets very large?

8. Suppose A < 0. How are the graphs affected?

Animation Option

In Question 1, set **Step** = .5, **A** = 1, **B** = 1.1, and **Max** = 5. Press **GRAPH** to animate.

Exponential Graphs

Activity Objective

Students use the Transformation Graphing App to explore how values of *a* and *b* affect the graph of $y = ab^x$.

Correlation to Text

- Lesson 8-7: Exponential Functions

Time

- 25–30 minutes

Materials/Software

- Transformation Graphing App
- Program: **A1L87**
- Activity worksheet

Skills Needed

- change parameter values

Classroom Management

- Students can work individually or in pairs depending on the number of calculators available.
- Circulate around the room as students work to help individuals and groups discover the concepts.

Notes

- Reminder: As noted on p. vi, each Activity page assumes that you activate the appropriate App at the start of the activity.
- Students can enter values for A and B directly by typing the number and pressing ENTER .
- By the end of the activity, discuss A as the *y*-intercept, a starting place, and B reflecting a rate of growth or decay.
- Students should uninstall the Transformation Graphing App at the end of this activity and then run DEFAULT.

Answers

1. The *y*-intercept increases.   2. The graph rises more quickly.   3. No; as *x* increases, *y* increases.

4. The horizontal line $y = 8$. The function becomes $y = 8(1)^x$ or $y = 8$.

5. The graph gets closer and closer to the *x*-axis.

6. A horizontal line through $y = A$; a decay function with A as the *y*-intercept; a growth function with A as the *y*-intercept; the graph rises more quickly; the graph gets closer and closer to the *x*-axis.

7. Y gets very close to zero.

8. The graphs reflect across the *x*-axis.

Exponential Function Match

For Use With Lesson 8-8

> **FILES NEEDED:** Transformation Graphing App
> Program: **A1L88**

A1L88 graphs the exponential function $y = ab^x$ as Y1 = AB^X with
A = 1 and B = 1.1.

In this activity you will see three scatter plots, one
at a time. You are to change the A and B values for
Y1 = AB^X until you find a function $y = ab^x$ that is
a perfect match for the given plot.

1. Run **A1L88**. Find an exponential function
   whose graph matches the plot.

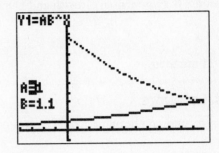

2. Switch from **Plot1** to **Plot2**. Press **GRAPH** to see **A1L88** for the
   second plot. Find a matching exponential function.

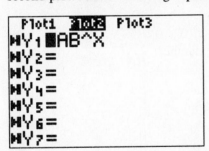

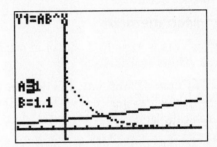

3. Switch from **Plot2** to **Plot3**. Press **GRAPH**
   to see **A1L88** for the third plot. Find a
   matching exponential function.

4. By looking at the graphs, how can you tell
   whether to use values of B with B > 1 or
   with 0 < B < 1?

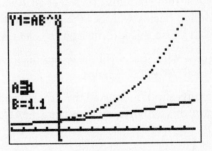

Exponential Function Match

Activity Objective

Students use the Transformation Graphing App to learn how changing the values of *a* and *b* affects the graph of $y = ab^x$.

Correlation to Text

- Lesson 8-8: Exponential Growth and Decay

Time

- 20–25 minutes

Materials/Software

- Transformation Graphing App
- Program: **A1L88**
- Activity worksheet

Skills Needed

- change parameter values
- select and deselect a plot

Classroom Management

- Students can work individually or in pairs depending on the number of calculators available.
- Use TI Connect™ software, TI-GRAPH LINK™ software, the TI-Navigator™ system, or unit-to-unit links to transfer **A1L88** to each calculator.

Notes

- Suggest that students first select an **A** value that matches the *y*-intercept and then decide whether the graph shows growth (**B** > 1) or decay (**B** < 1). Use this information to select a starting value for **B**.
- Discuss with students how to deselect and select a plot in either the **Y=** or **STAT PLOT** screens.
- Students should uninstall the Transformation Graphing App at the end of this activity and then run **DEFAULT**.

Answers

1. $y = 10(0.9)^x$

2. $y = 6(0.65)^x$

3. $y = 1(1.25)^x$

4. If the graph "grows," or rises to the right, use **B** > 1. If it shows decay, use 0 < **B** < 1.

Multiplying Binomials

For Use With Lesson 9-3

FILES NEEDED: Cabri® Jr.
AppVar: **A1L93**

A1L93 shows the area model for the product of two binomials.

1. Each rectangle in the model has length, width, and area. For the first diagram shown in **A1L93** (at the right), list the length, width, and area of each of the five rectangles below.

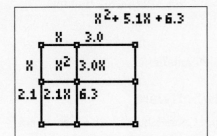

Rectangle	Length	Width	Area
top left			
top right			
bottom left			
bottom right			
large rectangle			

2. You can change the dimensions of the rectangle by dragging the top-right vertex and the lower-left vertex. Change both dimensions and complete the table below for your new model.

Rectangle	Length	Width	Area
top left			
top right			
bottom left			
bottom right			
large rectangle			

3. Predict the values that complete the table below. Then test your predictions.

Rectangle	Length	Width	Area
top left	x	x	
top right	4		
bottom left		2	
bottom right			
large rectangle			

Extension

4. Use pencil and paper. Generalize the model by drawing a diagram and making a table for which the top-right rectangle has length a and the bottom left rectangle has width b.

Multiplying Binomials

Activity Objective

Students use Cabri® Jr. to develop understanding of how to multiply binomials.

Correlation to Text

- Lesson 9-3: Multiplying Binomials

Time

- 15–20 minutes

Materials/Software

- App: Cabri® Jr.
- Program: A1L93
- Activity worksheet

Skills Needed

- drag a point

Classroom Management

- Students can work individually or in pairs depending on the number of calculators available.
- Use TI Connect™ software, TI-GRAPH LINK™ software, the TI-Navigator™ system, or unit-to-unit links to transfer A1L93 to each calculator.

Notes

- Remind students that Cabri® Jr. rounds values to the nearest tenth.

Answers

1.

Rectangle	Length	Width	Area
top left	x	x	x^2
top right	3.0	x	$3.0x$
bottom left	x	2.1	$2.1x$
bottom right	3.0	2.1	6.3
large rectangle	$x + 3.0$	$x + 2.1$	$x^2 + 5.1x + 6.3$

2. Check students' work.

3.

Rectangle	Length	Width	Area
top left	x	x	x^2
top right	4	x	$4x$
bottom left	x	2	$2x$
bottom right	4	2	8
large rectangle	$x + 4$	$x + 2$	$x^2 + 6x + 8$

4. The large rectangle should have length $x + a$, width $x + b$, and area $(x + a)(x + b) = x^2 + (a + b)x + ab$.

Square of a Binomial

For Use With Lesson 9-4

FILES NEEDED: Cabri® Jr.

AppVar: **A1L94**

A1L94 shows the area model for the square of a binomial.

1. Each rectangle in the model has length, width, and area. For the first diagram shown in **A1L94** (at the right), list the length, width, and area of each of the five rectangles below

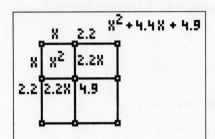

Rectangle	Length	Width	Area
top left			
top right			
bottom left			
bottom right			
large square			

2. The large figure above is a square. Given that the top-left rectangle in the figure is also a square, what must be true about the bottom-right rectangle? About the other two rectangles? Justify each answer.

3. You can change the dimensions of the large square by dragging the bottom-left vertex. Change the dimensions and complete the table below for your new model.

	Length	Width	Area
top left square			
each rectangle			
other inside square			
large square			

4. Predict the values you would get for each of the following when the two inside squares have lengths x and 2.5. Then test your predictions.

Area of each rectangle   Area of large square

Extension

5. Use pencil and paper. Generalize the model by drawing a diagram and making a table for which the large square has length $x + a$.

Square of a Binomial

Activity Objective

Students use Cabri® Jr. to develop understanding of how to square a binomial.

Correlation to Text

- Lesson 9-4: Multiplying Special Cases

Time

- 15–20 minutes

Materials/Software

- App: Cabri® Jr.
- Program: A1L94
- Activity worksheet

Skills Needed

- drag a point

Classroom Management

- Students can work individually or in pairs depending on the number of calculators available.
- Use TI Connect™ software, TI-GRAPH LINK™ software, the TI-Navigator™ system, or unit-to-unit links to transfer A1L94 to each calculator.

Notes

- Remind students that Cabri® Jr. rounds values to the nearest tenth.

Answers

1.

Rectangle	Length	Width	Area
top left	x	x	x^2
top right	2.2	x	$2.2x$
bottom left	x	2.2	$2.2x$
bottom right	2.2	2.2	4.9
large rectangle	$x + 2.2$	$x + 2.2$	$x^2 + 4.4x + 4.9$

2. It is a square. The other two rectangles are congruent. Check students' work.

3. Check students' work.

4. $2.5x; x^2 + 5x + 6.25$

5.

	Length	Width	Area
top left square	x	x	x^2
each rectangle	a	x	ax
other inside square	a	a	a^2
large square	$x + a$	$x + a$	$x^2 + 2ax + a^2$

Quadratic Graphs I

For Use With Lesson 10-1

FILES NEEDED: Transformation Graphing App
Program: **A1L101**

A1L101 graphs the quadratic function $y = ax^2 + c$ as Y1 = AX^2 + C.

In this activity, you will explore the graph of $y = ax^2 + c$.

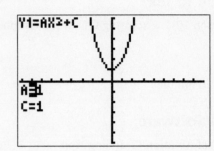

1. Run A1L101. Set **Step** = .2 and increment the value of **A** in steps of 1. When **A** > 0, what happens to the graph as **A** increases?

2. Decrease the value of **A**. What happens to the graph as **A** decreases? What happens to the graph as **A** gets close to zero but remains greater than zero?

3. Set **A** = −0.5. Describe the graph.

4. Try several different negative values for **A**. What happens to the graph as **A** gets close to zero?

5. For what values of **A** does the parabola open up? Open down?

6. What happens to the parabola when **A** = 0? Explain why this makes sense, given your answers to Questions 2 and 4.

Set **A** = 1, **Step** = 1, and select **C**.

7. Increase the value of **C**. What happens to the graph as **C** increases?

8. Predict what will happen to the graph as **C** decreases. Test your prediction.

Extension

The *vertex* is the highest or lowest point on the parabola.

9. What are the coordinates of the vertex of the parabola with **A** = 2 and **C** = −3? Test your guess.

10. Choose values of **A** and **C** such that the vertex of the parabola is the highest point and is located at $(0, 5)$. Test your choices.

11. Find quadratic functions whose graphs are like those in this activity, except that their vertexes are at different places along the *x*-axis.

Quadratic Graphs I

Activity Objective

Students use the Transformation Graphing App to explore the graph of the parabola for the $y = ax^2 + c$ form.

Correlation to Text

- Lesson 10-1: Exploring Quadratic Graphs

Time

- 15–20 minutes

Materials/Software

- Transformation Graphing App
- Program: A1L101
- Activity worksheet

Skills Needed

- change parameter values
- change Step values

Classroom Management

- Students can work individually or in pairs depending on the number of calculators available.
- Encourage students to discuss their observations with other students.

Notes

- Students can enter values for A and B directly by typing the number and pressing ENTER .
- Students should uninstall the Transformation Graphing App at the end of this activity and then run DEFAULT to reset their calculators.
- Press WINDOW and change Step values in the SETTINGS menu.

Answers

1. The parabola gets narrower.

2. The parabola gets wider.

3. The parabola is wide and opens downward.

4. The parabola flattens upward.

5. For A > 0, the parabola opens up. For A < 0, the parabola opens down.

6. It becomes the horizontal line Y = 0. Since A = 0 is neither positive nor negative, the parabola does not open up *or* down.

7. The parabola moves up.

8. The parabola will move down.

9. $(0, -3)$

10. Answers may vary. Sample: A = −2, C = 5

11. Check students' work.

Quadratic Graphs II

For Use With Lesson 10-2

> **FILES NEEDED:** Transformation Graphing App
> Program: **A1L102A**

A1L102A graphs the quadratic function $y = ax^2 + bx$ as Y1 = AX^2 + BX.

In this activity, you will explore the graph of $y = ax^2 + bx$. The program **A1L102A** includes a grid that shows a dot at each integer in the x- and y-directions.

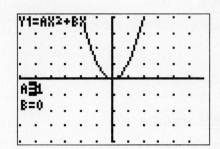

1. Run **A1L102A**. Select **B** and increment it in steps of 1. What happens to the vertex of the parabola as **B** increases?

2. Set **B** = −4. Complete the table below.

A	1	1	1	1	1
B	−4	−2	0	2	4
x-coordinate of vertex					

3. Use what you observed in Questions 1 and 2. How far does the vertex move horizontally each time you increase **B** by 1?

4. Set **A** = 2 and **B** = −4. Complete the table below.

A	2	2	2	2	2
B	−4	−2	0	2	4
x-coordinate of vertex					

5. Use what you observed in Question 4. How far does the vertex move horizontally each time you increase **B** by 1 when **A** = 2?

6. Complete this conjecture.

   For $y = ax^2 + bx$, the x-coordinate of the vertex of the graph is $\dfrac{b}{\blacksquare}$.

Extension

7. Use your ■ value from Question 6. Discuss the graph for ■ = 0.

8. Set **A** = 1 and **B** = −4. As you increment **B**, follow the path of the vertex. What kind of curve does it appear to trace? Give a convincing argument to support your answer.

Quadratic Graphs II

Activity Objective

Students use the Transformation Graphing App to explore the graph of the function $y = ax^2 + bx$ and the coordinates of the vertex of the parabola.

Correlation to Text

- Lesson 10-2: Quadratic Functions

Time

- 15–20 minutes

Materials/Software

- Transformation Graphing App
- Program: A1L102A
- Activity worksheet

Skills Needed

- change parameter values

Classroom Management

- Students can work individually or in pairs depending on the number of calculators available.
- Use TI Connect™ software, TI-GRAPH LINK™ software, the TI-Navigator™ system, or unit-to-unit links to transfer A1L102A to each calculator.

Notes

- You may wish to have students complete this activity before studying Lesson 10-2.
- Students can enter values for A and B directly by typing the number and pressing ENTER.
- Students should uninstall the Transformation Graphing App at the end of this activity and then run DEFAULT.

Answers

1. It moves to the left and down.   2. $2; 1; 0; -1, -2$ 3. $-\frac{1}{2}$ unit

4. $1; \frac{1}{2}; 0; -\frac{1}{2}; 1$ 5. $-\frac{1}{4}$ unit   6. $-2a$

7. If $-2a = 0$, then $a = 0$, and $y = bx$, which is the equation of a line.

8. Answers may vary. Sample: Since A is constant, the shape of the parabola does not change. C = 0 so the parabola always passes through $(0, 0)$. The effect is to view the parabola as a solid object that is sliding through an opening at the origin. For Y1 = X^2 + BX, the vertex is at X = $\frac{-B}{2}$, so the vertex follows the path of Y1 = $\left(\frac{-B}{2}\right)^2 + B\left(\frac{-B}{2}\right) = -\frac{1}{4}B^2$, a parabola that opens down.

Quadratic Function Match I

For Use With Lesson 10-2

FILES NEEDED: Transformation Graphing App
Program: **A1L102B**

A1L102B graphs the quadratic function $y = ax^2 + bx$ as $Y1 = AX^2 + BX$
with A = 1 and B = 0.

In this activity you will see three plots, one at a time. You are to change
the A and B values for $Y1 = AX^2 + BX$ until you find a function
$y = ax^2 + bx$ that is a perfect match for the given plot.

1. Run **A1L102B**. Find a quadratic function
whose graph matches the given plot, shown
at the right.

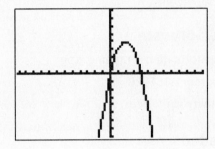

2. Switch from **Plot1** to **Plot2**. Press GRAPH to see **A1L102B** for the
second plot. Find a matching quadratic function.

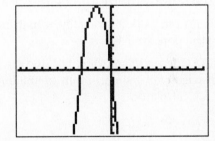

3. Switch from **Plot2** to **Plot3**. Press
GRAPH to see **A1L102B** for the third
plot. Find a matching quadratic function.

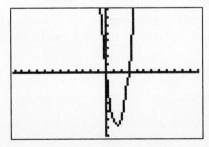

4. By looking at the graphs, how can you tell
that none of the functions you seek would
have the form $y = ax^2 + c$?

Quadratic Function Match I

Activity Objective

Students use the Transformation Graphing App to learn how changing the values of a and b affects the graph of $y = ax^2 + bx$.

Correlation to Text

- Lesson 10-2: Quadratic Functions

Time

- 15–20 minutes

Materials/Software

- Transformation Graphing App
- Program A1L102B
- Activity worksheet

Skills Needed

- change parameter values
- select and deselect a plot

Classroom Management

- Students can work individually or in pairs depending on the number of calculators available.
- Use TI Connect™ software, TI-GRAPH LINK™ software, the TI-Navigator™ system, or unit-to-unit links to transfer A1L102B to each calculator.

Notes

- Remind students that they can enter values directly for A= or B=. Type the value; then press ENTER .
- Students should uninstall the Transformation Graphing App at the end of this activity and then run DEFAULT.

Answers

1. $y = -x^2 + 4x$

2. $y = -2x^2 - 8x$

3. $y = 3x^2 - 9x$

4. None of the given graphs have the vertex on the y-axis. To have $y = ax^2 + c$ form, the vertex would be on the y-axis.

Graphs, Solutions, and Factors

For Use Before Lesson 10-5

FILES NEEDED: Transformation Graphing App
Program: **A1L105**

In A1L105, the quadratic function $y = (x - a)(x - b)$ is in *factored form* and is graphed as Y1 = (X – A)(X – B).

In this activity, you will explore relationships among
- the *x*-intercepts of a quadratic function,
- the solutions of the related quadratic equation, and
- the factors of the related quadratic expression.

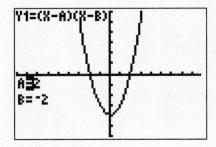

1. Run **A1L105**. For the graph that appears, what are the initial values given for **A** and **B**? What are the *x*-intercepts of the graph?

2. Change the value of **A**. What happens to the values of the *x*-intercepts of the graph when you change **A**? Change the value of **A** again to check what you have observed.

3. Set **A** = 2. Select **B** and change its value. What happens to the values of the *x*-intercepts when you change **B**? Change the value of **B** again to check what you have observed.

4. Complete this conjecture.

   The *x*-intercepts of the graph of $y = (x - a)(x - b)$ are __?__ .

5. Use your answer to Question 4 to predict the *x*-intercepts of the graph of the quadratic function $y = (x - 1)(x - 5)$. Set **A** = 1 and **B** = 5 to check your prediction.

6. The quadratic function $y = (x - a)(x - b)$ has $(x - a)(x - b) = 0$ as its *related quadratic equation*. Explain why the *x*-intercepts of the graph of the quadratic function are the solutions of the related equation.

7. The quadratic function $y = x^2 - 5x + 6$ is in standard form. Write it in factored form. Predict the *x*-intercepts of its graph and the solutions of the equation $x^2 - 5x + 6 = 0$. Use **A1L105** to check your predictions.

Extension

8. Describe what happens to the graph of $y = (x - a)(x - b)$ as you bring the values of **A** and **B** closer together.

9. When **A** = **B**, what appears to be true about the graph? What does this mean in terms of solutions of the related quadratic equation?

Graphs, Solutions, and Factors

Activity Objective

Students use the Transformation Graphing App to explore the relationships among the x-intercepts of a quadratic function, the solutions of the related quadratic equation, and the factors of the related quadratic expression.

Correlation to Text

- Lesson 10-5: Factoring to Solve Quadratic Equations

Time

- 15–20 minutes

Materials/Software

- Transformation Graphing App
- Program: A1L105
- Activity worksheet

Skills Needed

- change a parameter

Classroom Management

- Students can work individually or in pairs depending on the number of calculators available.
- Use TI Connect™ software, TI-GRAPH LINK™ software, the TI-Navigator™ system, or unit-to-unit links to transfer A1L105 to each calculator.

Notes

- Students should complete this activity before studying Lesson 10-5.
- Students should uninstall the Transformation Graphing App at the end of this activity and then run **DEFAULT** to reset their calculators.

Answers

1. $2, -2; 2, -2$

2. One x-intercept moves with the value of B.

3. The other x-intercept moves with the value of B.

4. a, b

5. $1, 5$

6. If $x = a$ then $(x - a) = 0$ and $(x - a)(x - b) = 0$.
   Likewise, if $x = b$ then $(x - b) = 0$ and $(x - a)(x - b) = 0$.

7. $y = (x - 3)(x - 2); 3, 2$

8. The x-intercepts move closer together. The vertex gets closer to the x-axis.

9. The vertex sits on the x-axis. There is only one solution to the related quadratic equation.

The Discriminant

For Use With Lesson 10-8

FILES NEEDED: Transformation Graphing App
Program: A1L108

In A1L108, the quadratic function $y = ax^2 + bx + c$ is in standard form.
It is graphed as Y1 = AX^2 + BX + C. The related quadratic equation is
$ax^2 + bx + c = 0$.

In this activity, you will explore the relationship between the value of
$b^2 - 4ac$ and the number of solutions of the related quadratic equation.

1. Recall: How do the number of x-intercepts of the graph of a
   quadratic function relate to the number of solutions of the
   corresponding quadratic equation? (*Hint:* What is the value of the
   function at an x-intercept?)

2. Run A1L108. Find four sets of values for A,
   B, and C so the parabola intersects the x-axis
   exactly once. Record A, B, C, and the values
   of B^2 – 4AC in the table below.

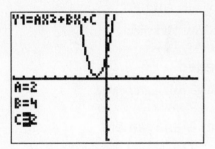

A				
B				
C				
B^2 – 4AC				

3. Study the data in the table. Complete this conjecture about the relationship
   between a quadratic equation with one solution and the value of $b^2 - 4ac$.

   The graph of $y = ax^2 + bx + c$ has one x-intercept and the related equation
   $ax^2 + bx + c = 0$ has one solution if $b^2 - 4ac$ = __?__.

4. Find four sets of A, B, C values so the parabola does *not* intersect the
   x-axis. Record A, B, C, and the values of B^2 – 4AC in the table below.

A				
B				
C				
B^2 – 4AC				

5. Study the data in the table. Make a conjecture about the relationship between a
   quadratic equation with no solutions and the value of $b^2 - 4ac$.

6. Study your conjectures from Questions 3 and 5. Make a conjecture about the
   relationship between a quadratic equation with two solutions and the value of
   $b^2 - 4ac$. Find values for a, b, and c that give a desired value of $b^2 - 4ac$. Then
   test your conjecture in A1L108.

The Discriminant

Activity Objective

Students use the Transformation Graphing App to discover the relationship between the number of solutions of a quadratic equation and the value of the discriminant.

Correlation to Text

- Lesson 10-8: Using the Discriminant

Time

- 15–20 minutes

Materials/Software

- Transformation Graphing App
- Program: A1L108
- Activity worksheet

Skills Needed

- change parameter values

Classroom Management

- Students can work individually or in pairs depending on the number of calculators available.
- Use TI Connect™ software, TI-GRAPH LINK™ software, the TI-Navigator™ system, or unit-to-unit links to transfer A1L108 to each calculator.

Notes

- Students should complete this activity before studying Lesson 10-8.
- Remind students that seeing many cases of a situation does *not* prove that the situation is always true!
- Students should uninstall the Transformation Graphing App at the end of this activity and then run DEFAULT to reset their calculators.

Answers

1. They are the same.
2. Check students' work.
3. 0
4. Check students' work.
5. If a quadratic equation has no solutions, then $b^2 - 4ac < 0$.
6. If a quadratic equation has two solutions, then $b^2 - 4ac > 0$.

Choose a Model I

For Use With Lesson 10-9

FILES NEEDED: Transformation Graphing App
Program: A1L109

In A1L109, the scatter plot suggests a relationship
between *x* and *y* values.

In this activity, you will explore ways to use the
Transformation Graphing App to help you find a
reasonable model for the relationship.

1. A good first step is to recall the models
   you have learned:
   - linear
   - quadratic
   - exponential

   Then you think, "Which of a line, a parabola, or an exponential
   curve could fit the scatter plot very well?" Which two of these three
   types of functions would give a reasonably good answer? Explain.

The general forms of these models are
$$y = mx + b \qquad y = ax^2 + bx + c \qquad y = ab^x$$

On your graphing calculator, these could appear as
$$Y1 = AX + B \qquad Y2 = AX^2 + BX + C \qquad Y3 = AB\char94 X$$

The numbers *a*, *b*, and *c* are called *parameters*. Choose two of Y1, Y2, and Y3
(match your choices from Question 1) to use for the following questions.

2. Run A1L109. Select one of your functions by highlighting the equal
   sign. Press GRAPH , then change its parameter values until graph points
   are close to given data points. Write the function for your graph.

3. As a check, find the Y-value for X = 5 and the Y-value of the data
   point at *x* = 5. How do they compare?

4. Select your second function by highlighting its equal sign. Change its
   parameter values until the points on the graph are close to the given
   data points. Write the function for this second graph.

5. Repeat the check of Question 3 for this function.

6. Which of the functions found in Questions 2 and 4 seem to work the
   best for the given data, or can you tell? You may find it helpful to
   highlight both of the equal signs and draw both graphs in the same
   window. Explain your choice.

Extension

7. Adjust the window settings to look at data points with *x*-values
   between 10 and 20. What can you conclude?

Choose a Model I

Activity Objective

Students use the Transformation Graphing App to compare quadratic and linear models.

Correlation to Text

- Lesson 10-9: Choosing a Model

Time

- 20–30 minutes

Materials/Software

- Transformation Graphing App
- Program: A1L109
- Activity worksheet

Skills Needed

- change parameter values
- select a function

Classroom Management

- Students can work individually or in pairs depending on the number of calculators available.
- Use TI Connect™ software, TI-GRAPH LINK™ software, the TI-Navigator™ system, or unit-to-unit links to transfer A1L109 to each calculator.

Notes

- Remind students that their models are likely to be different.
- Students may need to enter decimal values to hundredths to model the given data.
- Students can use **value** in the **CALC** menu to help answer Question 2.
- Students should uninstall the Transformation Graphing App at the end of this activity and then run **DEFAULT** to reset their calculators.

Answers

Answers may vary. Samples are given:

1. Quadratic or exponential model; their graphs are curved as is the scatter plot.

2. $y = 0.08x^2 - 1.2x + 4.9$ **3.** 0.9; 1.2   **4.** $y = 4.1(0.8)^x$ **5.** $\approx 1.3; 1.2$

6. Check students' work.

7. The quadratic function does not model the data well because its graph rises for $x > 10$ while the data y-values continue to decrease.

Square Root Graphs

For Use With Lesson 11-6

FILES NEEDED: Transformation Graphing App
Program: A1L116A

A1L116A graphs the square root function
$y = a\sqrt{x - b} + c$ as Y1 = A$\sqrt{}$ (X – B) + C.

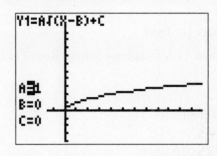

In this activity, you will explore the graph of the
square root function.

1. Write this function with A = 1, B = 0, and
   C = 0. This function is sometimes called the
   square root function. What is its domain?

2. Run A1L116A. Increment the value of B in steps of 1 or −1.
   What happens to the graph as B increases? As B decreases?

3. Set B = 4. What is the domain of the function for B = 4?

4. Set B = −1. What is the domain of the function for B = −1?

5. Set B = 1 and then select C. Change the value of C. How does the
   value of C affect the graph of the function?

6. Set C = 3. What is the range of the function?

7. Predict the domain and range of $y = \sqrt{x - 2} + 4$. Test your
   predictions by setting B and C to the correct values in A1L116A.

8. Write a function that has domain $x \geq -2$ and range $y \geq 5$. Graph
   your function to check the domain and range.

9. Set A, B, and C to match the screen at the
   right. Increment the value of A in steps of 1.
   What effect does this have on the graph?

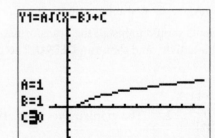

10. What happens to the graph when A < 0?
    (*Hint:* Try A = −0.5, A = −1, and A = −2.)

11. What happens if A = 0? Explain.

Extension

12. Each graph shown above is half of a parabola. For each screen, find
    a quadratic function whose graph, cut in half, has the same shape.
    (*Hint:* It will open upwards or downwards.) Justify your answer.

13. Describe how the effects of changing a, b, and c in $y = a\sqrt{x - b} + c$ and
    in $y = a|x - b| + c$ are similar.

Square Root Graphs

Activity Objective

Students use the Transformation Graphing App to explore how values of a, b, and c affect the graph of $y = a\sqrt{x - b} + c$.

Correlation to Text

- Lesson 11-6: Graphing Square Root Functions

Time

- 15–20 minutes

Materials/Software

- Transformation Graphing App.
- Program: A1L116A
- Activity worksheet

Skills Needed

- change parameter values

Classroom Management

- Students can work individually or in pairs depending on the number of calculators available.
- Use TI Connect™ software, TI-GRAPH LINK™ software, the TI-Navigator™ system, or unit-to-unit links to transfer A1L116A to each calculator.

Notes

- Use the term "translation" when appropriate.
- Remind students that the form has a "$- b$," so when they are asked to discuss $y = a\sqrt{x - 2} + 4$ in Question 7, $b = 2$.
- Students should uninstall the Transformation Graphing App at the end of this activity and then run **DEFAULT** to reset their calculators.

Answers

1. $x \geq 0$
2. The graph moves to the right. The graph moves to the left.

3. $x \geq 4$
4. $x \geq -1$
5. It translates the graph up or down.

6. $y \geq 3$
7. $x \geq 2, y \geq 4$
8. $y = \sqrt{x + 2} + 5$

9. As A increases, the graph rises more steeply.

10. The graph "flips."
11. The graph becomes the horizontal line $y = 0$.

12. Answers may vary. Samples: first screen, $y = x^2$; second screen, $y = x^2 + 1$

13. a: stretches vertically; b: shifts each left or right; c: shifts each up or down.

Square Root Function Match

FILES NEEDED: Transformation Graphing App
Program: **A1L116B**

A1L116B graphs the square root function $y = a\sqrt{x - b} + c$ as
Y1 = A√ (X − B) + C with A = 1, B = 0, and C = 0.

In this activity you will see three plots, one at a time. You are to change
the A , B, and C values for Y1= A√ (X − B) + C until you find a function
$y = a\sqrt{x - b} + c$ that is a perfect match for the given plot.

1. Run **A1L116B**. Find a square root function
    whose graph matches the given plot, shown at
    the right.

    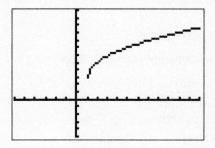

2. Switch from **Plot1** to **Plot2**. Press <u>GRAPH</u> to see **A1L116B** for the
    second plot. Find a matching square root function.

    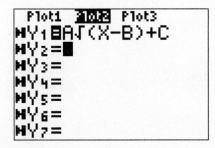   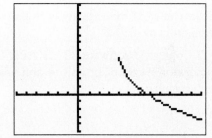

3. Switch from **Plot2** to **Plot3**. Press <u>GRAPH</u>
    to see **A1L116B** for the third plot. Find a
    matching square root function.

4. By looking at the graphs, how can you tell
    whether to use positive values for A or
    negative values for A?

    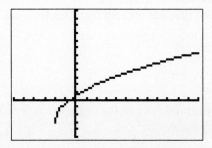

Square Root Function Match

Activity Objective

Students use the Transformation Graphing App to learn how changing the values of a, b, and c affects the graph of $y = a\sqrt{x - b} + c$.

Correlation to Text

- Lesson 11-6: Graphing Square Root Functions

Time

- 15–20 minutes

Materials/Software

- Transformation Graphing App
- Program: A1L116B
- Activity worksheet

Skills Needed

- change parameter values
- select and deselect plots

Classroom Management

- Students can work individually or in pairs depending on the number of calculators available.
- Use TI Connect™ software, TI-GRAPH LINK™ software, the TI-Navigator™ system, or unit-to-unit links to transfer A1L116B to each calculator.

Notes

- Suggest that students find the value of **B**, then **C**, then **A**.
- Students should uninstall the Transformation Graphing App at the end of this activity and then run **DEFAULT**.

Answers

1. $y = 2\sqrt{x - 1} + 3$ 2. $y = -3\sqrt{x - 4} + 5$ 3. $y = 2.5\sqrt{x + 2} - 3$

4. If the graph rises to the right, use **A** > 0. If the graph falls to the right, use **A** < 0.

Rational Graphs

For Use With Lesson 12-2

FILES NEEDED: Transformation Graphing App
Program: **A1L122A**

A1L122A graphs the rational function $y = \frac{a}{x-b} + c$ as
Y1 = (A/(X − B)) + C with A = 4, B = 0, and C = 0.

In this activity you will explore the graph of the rational function.

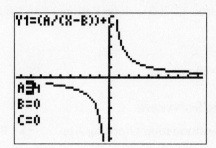

1. Run **A1L122A**. Change the value of **A**. What is the effect on the graph as **A** increases? As **A** decreases?

2. Predict the effects that you think the values **B** and **C** have on the graph of $y = \frac{a}{x-b} + c$. [*Hint:* Review the effects of **B** and **C** in "Absolute Value Graphs" (p. 13) and "Square Root Graphs" (p. 45).]

As $|x|$ gets large, the graph of the rational function $y = \frac{a}{x}$ ($b = 0, c = 0$) approaches a horizontal line (the x-axis in this case). As $|x|$ gets small, the graph approaches a vertical line (here, the y-axis). Any rational function has two such *asymptotes*. On the screen, you generally will not see them. On paper, you should draw the asymptotes to help you graph the function.

In the Questions that follow, observe (in your mind's eye) the asymptotes as you change values for **B** and **C**.

3. Increase the value of **B** to 2. What happens to the graph? To the asymptotes?

4. How does changing the value of **B** affect the graph? The asymptotes?

5. Predict the value for **B** that will put the vertical asymptote at −3? Test your prediction.

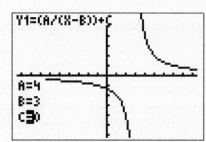

6. Set **B** = 3. Increase the value of **C**. Describe the effect of **C** on the graph?

7. Where is the horizontal asymptote for **C** = 4?

8. What equation will have a vertical asymptote at $x = -3$ and a horizontal asymptote at $y = 2$? Test your equation.

Extension

9. What type of variation does a rational function model when $b = 0$, and $c = 0$?

10. What happens to a rational function graph when you replace **A** by its opposite?

Rational Graphs

Activity Objective

Students use the Transformation Graphing App to explore how changing the values of a, b, and c affects the graph of $y = \frac{a}{x - b} + c$.

Correlation to Text

- Lesson 12-2: Graphing Rational Functions

Time

- 25–30 minutes

Materials/Software

- Transformation Graphing App
- Program: A1L122A
- Activity worksheet

Classroom Management

- Students can work individually or in pairs depending on the number of calculators available.
- Use TI Connect™ software, TI-GRAPH LINK™ software, the TI-Navigator™ system, or unit-to-unit links to transfer A1L122A to each calculator.

Notes

- Remind students that when they graph by hand, they should first locate and graph the asymptotes.
- Discuss why there are two asymptotes.
- Compare the translations of this function with the translations of the functions previously studied.
- Remind students that in Question 8 the denominator becomes $x - (-3)$, or $x + 3$.

Answers

1. As A increases, the graph moves farther from the origin. As A decreases the graph moves closer to the origin.

2. Changing B will translate the graph horizontally. Changing C will translate it vertically.

3. The graph translates 2 units to the right. The vertical asymptote becomes $x = 2$. The horizontal asymptote remains $y = 0$.

4. Changing B translates the graph and the vertical asymptote horizontally.

5. $B = -3$

6. Changing C translates the graph vertically.

7. $y = 4$

8. $y = \frac{a}{x + 3} + 2$

9. inverse variation

10. The graph reflects across the horizontal asymptote.

Rational Function Match

For Use With Lesson 12-2

FILES NEEDED: Transformation Graphing App
Programs: A1L122B, A1L122C, A1L122D

Each program above graphs the rational function $y = \frac{a}{x - b} + c$ as
Y1 = A/(X – B) + C with A = 2, B = 0, and C = 0.

The startup screen shows two asymptotes and plots 6 points for the graph of
a rational function. You are to change the values of A, B and C until you find
a function $y = \frac{a}{x - b} + c$ that is a perfect match for the given plot.

1. Run **A1L122B**. Find a rational function
    whose graph has the given asymptotes and
    contains the six given points.

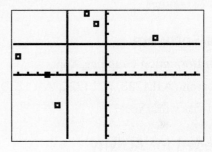

2. Run **A1L122C**. Find a rational function
    whose graph has the given asymptotes and
    contains the six given points.

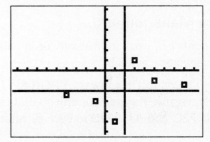

3. Run **A1L122D**. Find a rational function
    whose graph has the given asymptotes and
    contains the six given points.

4. By looking at the graphs, how can you tell
    whether to use positive values for A or
    negative values for A?

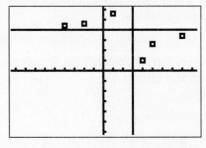

Rational Function Match

Activity Objective

Students use the Transformation Graphing App to study how changing parameter values affects the graph of $y = \frac{a}{x - b} + c$.

Correlation to Text

- Lesson 12-2: Graphing Rational Functions

Time

- 15–20 minutes

Materials/Software

- Transformation Graphing App
- Program: A1L122B, A1L122C, A1L122D
- Activity worksheet

Skills Needed for Activity

- change parameter values

Classroom Management

- Students can work individually or in pairs depending on the number of calculators available.
- Use TI Connect™ software, TI-GRAPH LINK™ software, the TI-Navigator™ system, or unit-to-unit links to transfer A1L122B, A1L122C, and A1L122D to each calculator.

Notes

- Point out the difference between asymptotes (no scale marks) and axes (scale marks).
- Encourage students to determine the value of B, then C, then A.
- Students should uninstall the Transformation Graphing App at the end of this activity and then run DEFAULT.

Answers

1. $y = \frac{6}{x + 4} + 3$
2. $y = \frac{3}{x - 2} - 2$
3. $y = \frac{-3}{x - 3} + 4$

4. If the graphs are to the lower left and upper right of the asymptotes, use A > 0. If the graphs are to the upper left and lower right of the asymptotes, use A < 0.

Perpendicular Bisectors

For Use With Lesson 1-5

FILES NEEDED: Cabri® Jr.
AppVar: GL15A

Given: In GL15A, point *T* is on line 1, the perpendicular bisector of $\overline{AB}$.

Explore: properties of the perpendicular bisector

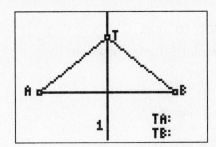

1. Drag point *T* along line 1. Find lengths *TA* and *TB* for four different locations of *T*. Collect your data in the table below.

Length *TA*				
Length *TB*				

2. Drag point *A* or *B* to change the length of $\overline{AB}$. Find lengths *TA* and *TB* for four lengths of $\overline{AB}$. Collect your data in the table below.

Length *TA*				
Length *TB*				

3. Study the data in each table. Complete this conjecture about how lengths *TA* and *TB* are related.

   If point *T* is on the perpendicular bisector of segment $\overline{AB}$,
   then *TA* = __?__ .

4. Generalize your conjecture from Question 3. Use just one word for the blank below.

   If a point is on the perpendicular bisector of a segment, then the point is __?__ from the endpoints of the segment.

Extension

5. Suppose you have a point *Q* in the diagram so that *QA* = *QB*. Make a conjecture about the location of point *Q*. Then test your conjecture. Draw point *Q*. Install measures *QA* and *QB*. Then drag *Q* to make *QA* = *QB*.

6. Suppose you have two segments, $\overline{AB}$ and $\overline{CD}$, not in the same line. Make a conjecture about the location of a point *Q* for which *QA* = *QB* and *QC* = *QD*. Test your conjecture.

Perpendicular Bisectors

Activity Objective

Students use Cabri® Jr. to explore the properties of perpendicular bisectors.

Correlation to Text

- Lesson 1-5: Basic Constructions

Time

- 10–15 minutes

Materials/Software

- App: Cabri® Jr.
- AppVar: GL15A
- Activity worksheet

Skills Needed

- drag an object
- install a measure

Classroom Management

- Students can work individually or in pairs depending on the number of calculators available.
- Use TI Connect™ software, TI-GRAPH LINK™ software, the TI-Navigator™ system, or unit-to-unit links to transfer **GL15A** to each calculator.

Notes

- Reminder: As noted on p. vi, each Activity page assumes that you activate the appropriate App at the start of the activity.
- In **F1**, select **Open** and then press ENTER to see the AppVar list.
- Dragging point A or B will change the orientation of the diagram but will not affect the perpendicular bisector relationship.
- If students change the length of $\overline{AB}$ by dragging either Point A or Point B, the length TA will still equal the length TB.

Answers

1–2. Check students' work.   **3.** *TB*   **4.** equidistant

5. Point Q must be on line l.

6. Q is on the perpendicular bisector of both $\overline{AB}$ and $\overline{CD}$.

Angle Bisectors

For Use With Lesson 1-5

FILES NEEDED: Cabri® Jr.
AppVar: **GL15B**

Given: In GL15B, $\overline{PR}$ is the bisector of $\angle CPD$.
Point T is on $\overline{PR}$. Points A and B are on
the sides of the angle. $\overline{TA}$ and $\overline{TB}$ are
perpendicular to the sides.

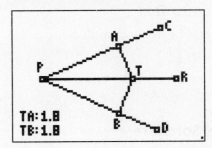

TA:1.8
TB:1.8

Explore: the properties of the angle bisector

1. Drag point T along $\overline{PR}$. Find lengths TA
and TB for four different locations of T.
Collect your data in the table below.

Length TA				
Length TB				

Open **GL15B** again. This returns you to the original figure.

2. Drag point C or D to change the size of $\angle CPD$. Find lengths
TA and TB for four sizes of $\angle CPD$. Collect your data in the
table below.

Length TA				
Length TB				

3. Study the data in each table. Complete this conjecture
about how lengths TA and TB are related.

If point T is on the bisector of $\angle CPD$, and $\overline{TA}$ and $\overline{TB}$ are
perpendicular to the sides of the angle at points A and B,
respectively, then $TA = \underline{\ ?\ }$.

4. The length of the perpendicular segment from a point to a line
is the *distance from the point to the line*. Use this to help you
generalize your conjecture from Question 3. Use just one word
for the blank below.

A point on the bisector of an angle is $\underline{\ ?\ }$ from the sides of
the angle.

Extension

5. Suppose you add a point Z to the diagram with the property that the
lengths of the perpendicular segments from Z to sides $\overline{PC}$ and $\overline{PD}$
are equal. Make a conjecture about the location of point Z. Test
your conjecture.

Angle Bisectors

Activity Objective

Students use Cabri® Jr. to explore the properties of angle bisectors.

Correlation to Text

- Lesson 1-5: Basic Constructions

Time

- 10–15 minutes

Materials/Software

- App: Cabri® Jr.
- AppVar GL15B
- Activity worksheet

Skills Needed

- drag an object
- install a measure

Classroom Management

- Students can work individually or in pairs depending on the number of calculators available.
- Use TI Connect™ software, TI-GRAPH LINK™ software, the TI-Navigator™ system, or unit-to-unit links to transfer GL15B to each calculator.

Notes

- In F1, select Open and then press **ENTER** to see the AppVar list.
- Segments are used rather than rays because Cabri® Jr. does not support the construction of rays.
- Students can change $\angle CPD$ by dragging points C, P, or D.

Answers

1–2. Check students' work.

3. *TB*

4. equidistant

5. Point Z is on angle bisector $\overline{PR}$.

Linear Pairs

> **FILES NEEDED:** Cabri® Jr.
> AppVar: **GL24**

Given: In GL24, Point O is on $\overleftrightarrow{AC}$. Point B is not
on $\overleftrightarrow{AC}$. $\angle AOB$ and $\angle BOC$ are a linear pair
of angles.

Explore: the angle measures of a linear pair

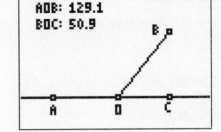

1. Drag point B to four different locations. Find
   $m\angle AOB$ and $m\angle BOC$ for each location. Collect
   your data in the table below.

2. For each location, find the sum of the measures of
   $\angle AOB$ and $\angle BOC$.

$m\angle AOB$				
$m\angle BOC$				
$m\angle AOB + m\angle BOC$				

3. Study the data in the table. Complete this conjecture about the sum
   of the measures of $\angle AOB$ and $\angle BOC$.

   If $\angle AOB$ and $\angle BOC$ are a linear pair, then __?__ .

4. Generalize your conjecture from Question 3.

   If two angles form a linear pair, then __?__ .

Extension

5. Drag point B so that $m\angle AOB = m\angle BOC$. What must be true about
   $\overrightarrow{OB}$ and $\overleftrightarrow{AC}$? Explain.

6. Drag B so that $m\angle BOC = 3\ m\angle BOC$. What are the measures of
   each angle? Verify your answer using algebra.

7. Write a problem similar to Question 6 that can be answered by
   dragging B and then verified algebraically. Give your question to a
   classmate to answer and verify.

Linear Pairs

Activity Objective

Students use Cabri® Jr. to explore properties of linear pairs.

Correlation to Text

- Lesson 2-4: Reasoning in Algebra

Time

- 10–15 minutes

Materials/Software

- App: Cabri® Jr.
- AppVar: **GL24**
- Activity worksheet

Skills Needed

- drag an object

Classroom Management

- Students can work individually or in pairs depending on the number of calculators available.
- Use TI Connect™ software, TI-GRAPH LINK™ software, the TI-Navigator™ system, or unit-to-unit links to transfer **GL24** to each calculator.

Notes

- In **F1**, select **Open** and then press **ENTER** to see the AppVar list.
- If the sums of the angle measures stay close to the same value, they should be considered equal.

Error Prevention

- Cabri® Jr. will not measure angles greater than 180°. Students should keep point B above $\overline{AC}$.

Answers

1–2. Check students' work.

3. $m\angle AOB + m\angle BOC = 180$ **4.** their sum is 180

5. They are perpendicular. If $x + y = 180$ and $x = y$, then $x = 90$.

6. $m\angle AOB = 135$, $m\angle BOC = 45$. If $x + y = 180$, and $x = 3y$, then $3y + y = 180$, $4y = 180$, $y = 45$, and $x = 135$.

7. Check students' work.

Vertical Angles

For Use With Lesson 2-5

> **FILES NEEDED:** Cabri® Jr.
> AppVar: GL25

Given: In GL25, $\overleftrightarrow{AC}$ and $\overleftrightarrow{BD}$ intersect at point O.

Explore: the angle measures of vertical angles

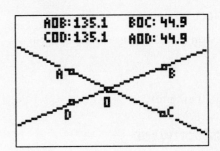

1. Drag point A or point B to four different locations. Find $m\angle AOB, m\angle BOC, m\angle COD$, and $m\angle AOD$ for each location. Collect your data in the table below.

$m\angle AOB$				
$m\angle BOC$				
$m\angle COD$				
$m\angle AOD$				

2. Identify the pairs of vertical angles.

3. Study the data in the table. Complete this conjecture about vertical angles.

    If $\angle AOB$ and __?__ are vertical angles, then __?__ .

4. Generalize your conjecture from Question 3.

    If two angles are vertical angles, then __?__ .

Extension

5. Drag point A or point B so that $m\angle AOB = m\angle BOC$. What must be true about $\overleftrightarrow{AC}$ and $\overleftrightarrow{BD}$?

Suppose you construct a third line as described. How many pairs of vertical angles can you find?

6. $\overleftrightarrow{EF}$ containing point O

7. $\overleftrightarrow{EF}$ containing point B

Animation Option

Instead of dragging point A or B in Question 1, animate A or B. Then stop the point at different locations to collect your data. (You can reset the animation by using Undo in the F1 menu.)

Vertical Angles

Activity Objective

Students use Cabri® Jr. to explore the properties of vertical angles.

Correlation to Text

- Lesson 2-5: Proving Angles Congruent

Time

- 15–20 minutes

Materials/Software

- App: Cabri® Jr.
- AppVar: **GL25**
- Activity worksheet

Skills Needed

- drag an object
- animate an object

Classroom Management

- Students can work individually or in pairs depending on the number of calculators available.
- Use TI Connect™ software, TI-GRAPH LINK™ software, the TI-Navigator™ system, or unit-to-unit links to transfer **GL25** to each calculator.

Notes

- Students can drag any labeled point except *O*.
- Students may answer the extension Questions 6 and 7 using reasoning or a drawing.

Answers

1. Check students' work.

2. $\angle AOB$ and $\angle COD$; $\angle BOC$ and $\angle AOD$

3. $\angle COD$; $m\angle AOB = m\angle COD$

4. their measures are equal

5. They are perpendicular.

6. 6 pairs

7. Answers may vary. Check students' work.

Parallel Lines, Related Angles

For Use With Lesson 3-1

> **FILES NEEDED:** Cabri® Jr.
> AppVar: GL31

Given: In GL31, $\overleftrightarrow{EF}$ intersects parallel lines $\overleftrightarrow{AB}$ and $\overleftrightarrow{CD}$ at points P and R.

Explore: relationships among angles formed by parallel lines and a transversal

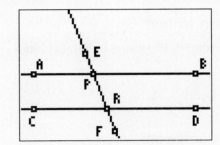

1. Complete the following. $\angle EPB$ and $\angle\underline{\ ?\ }$ are corresponding angles. Copy the name of the second angle into the first column of the table below.

$m\angle EPB$				
$m\angle$____				

2. Install the screen-angle measures for the two angles. Drag point E horizontally to four locations. Record each pair of angle measures in the table above.

3. Study the data in the table. Complete the following conjecture.

   For parallel lines and a transversal, if two angles are corresponding angles, then __?__ .

4. Drag point P to a location above point E and complete the following statement. The two angles you named as corresponding angles in Question 1 are now __?__ angles.

5. Copy the angle name from Question 1 into the two blanks in the first column of the table below. Record the two current angle measures and their sum in the second column.

$m\angle EPB$				
$m\angle$____				
$m\angle EPB + m\angle$____				

6. Drag point E horizontally to three other locations. Record the angle measures and their sum in the table.

7. Study the data in the table. Write a conjecture based on your data.

Animation Option

In Questions 2 and 6 you dragged point E. Instead, animate point E. Then stop it at different locations to collect your data. (You can reset the animation by using **Undo** in the **F1** menu.)

Parallel Lines, Related Angles

Activity Objective

Students use Cabri® Jr. to explore properties of corresponding and same-side interior angles.

Correlation to Text

- Lesson 3-1: Properties of Parallel Lines

Time

- 20–30 minutes

Materials/Software

- App: Cabri® Jr.
- AppVar: GL31
- Activity worksheet

Skills Needed

- install a measure
- drag an object
- animate an object

Classroom Management

- Students can work individually or in pairs depending on the number of calculators available.
- Use TI Connect™ software, TI-GRAPH LINK™ software, the TI-Navigator™ system, or unit-to-unit links to transfer GL31 to each calculator.

Notes

- In F1, select **Open** and then press **ENTER** to see the AppVar list.
- Students can drag points E and P. All other points are fixed, and line $\overleftrightarrow{AB}$ remains parallel to line $\overleftrightarrow{CD}$.

Error Prevention

- To install a screen-angle measure, be sure to choose a pre-existing point, which will flash when selected. If you do not select a pre-existing point, Cabri® Jr. will construct a new point which may not produce the desired results.

Answers

1–2. Check students' work.

3. they have equal measures

4. same-side interior

5–6. Check students' work.

7. Answers may vary. Sample: If two angles are same-side interior angles, they are supplementary.

Exterior Angle of a Triangle

For Use With Lesson 3-3

> **FILES NEEDED:** Cabri® Jr.
> AppVar: **GL33**

Given: In GL33, △*BCD* has
exterior angle ∠*ABD*.

Explore: the measures of exterior angles

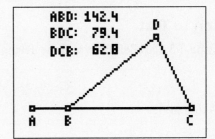

1. Drag point *B* to three different locations along
$\overline{AC}$. Find $m\angle ABD$, $m\angle BDC$, and $m\angle DCB$ for
each location. Collect your data in the first three
blank columns of the table below.

$m\angle ABD$						
$m\angle BDC$						
$m\angle DCB$						

2. Drag point *D* vertically to three new locations. Find three more sets
of values for $m\angle ABD$, $m\angle BDC$, and $m\angle DCB$. Record your data in
the last three columns of the table above.

3. Study the data in the table. Complete the following conjecture about
the exterior angle ∠*ABD* and its two remote interior angles, ∠*BDC*
and ∠*DCB*.

   If ∠*ABD* is an exterior angle of △*BCD*, then $m\angle ABD = \underline{\ ?\ }$.

4. Generalize your conjecture from Question 3.

   The measure of an exterior angle of a triangle is $\underline{\ ?\ }$.

Extension

5. How are $m\angle CBD$ and $m\angle ABD$ related?

6. How are $m\angle CBD$, $m\angle BDC$, and $m\angle DCB$ related?

7. Use your answers to Questions 5 and 6 to prove that your
conjecture in Question 3 is true.

Animation Option

In Question 1, instead of dragging point *B*, animate *B* and stop it at
different locations to collect your data. In Question 2, you can animate
point *D* to collect data. (You can reset the animation by using **Undo**
in the **F1** menu.)

Exterior Angle of a Triangle

Activity Objective

Students use Cabri® Jr. to explore the relationship between interior and exterior angles of a triangle.

Correlation to Text

- Lesson 3-3: Parallel Lines and the Triangle Angle-Sum Theorem

Time

- 15–20 minutes

Materials/Software

- App: Cabri® Jr.
- AppVar: GL33
- Activity worksheet

Skills Needed

- drag an object
- animate an object

Classroom Management

- Students can work individually or in pairs depending on the number of calculators available.
- Use TI Connect™ software, TI-GRAPH LINK™ software, the TI-Navigator™ system, or unit-to-unit links to transfer **GL33** to each calculator.

Notes

- Students can drag point B along $\overline{AC}$. Students can drag point D freely.

Answers

1–2. Check students' work.

3. $m\angle BDC + m\angle DCB$

4. equal to the sum of the measures of the two remote interior angles

5. $m\angle CBD + m\angle ABD = 180$.

6. $m\angle CBD + m\angle BDC + m\angle DCB = 180$.

7. By substitution, $m\angle CBD + m\angle ABD = m\angle CBD + m\angle BDC + m\angle DCB$.
Subtract $m\angle CBD$ from each side. $m\angle ABD = m\angle BDC + m\angle DCB$

Exterior Angle Sums

For Use With Lesson 3-4

· ·

FILES NEEDED: Cabri® Jr.
AppVars: GL34A, GL34B

Given: In GL34A, ∠1, ∠2, and ∠3 are exterior angles of the triangle.

Explore: the sum of the measures of exterior angles of a triangle

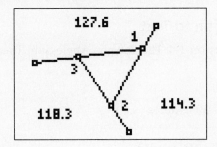

1. Drag any of the three vertices. Make four different triangles. For each triangle, find $m\angle1$, $m\angle2$, and $m\angle3$. Record their measures and their sum in the table below.

$m\angle1$				
$m\angle2$				
$m\angle3$				
$m\angle1 + m\angle2 + m\angle3$				

2. Study the data in the table. Complete this conjecture about the sum of the measures of the exterior angles of a triangle.

   The sum of the measures of the exterior angles of a triangle, one at each vertex, is __?__ .

Given: In GL34B, ∠1, ∠2, ∠3, and ∠4 are exterior angles of the quadrilateral.

Explore: the sum of the measures of exterior angles of a quadrilateral

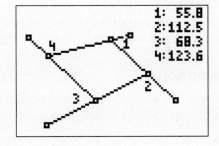

3. Open GL34B. Repeat Questions 1 and 2 for a quadrilateral. Record your data in the table below. Make a conjecture about the sum of the measures of the exterior angles of a quadrilateral.

$m\angle1$				
$m\angle2$				
$m\angle3$				
$m\angle4$				
$m\angle1 + m\angle2 + m\angle3 + m\angle4$				

Extension

4. Make a conjecture about the sum of the exterior angle measures of a pentagon.

· ·

Exterior Angle Sums

Activity Objective

Students use Cabri® Jr. to explore the sum of the measures of exterior angles of polygons.

Correlation to Text

- Lesson 3-4: The Polygon Angle-Sum Theorems

Time

- 20–30 minutes

Materials/Software

- App: Cabri® Jr.
- AppVars: **GL34A, GL34B**
- Activity worksheet

Skills Needed

- drag an object

Classroom Management

- Students can work individually or in pairs depending on the number of calculators available.
- Use TI Connect™ software, TI-GRAPH LINK™ software, the TI-Navigator™ system, or unit-to-unit links to transfer **GL34A** and **GL34B** to each calculator.

Error Prevention

- Be sure that students form convex quadrilaterals only. Using concave quadrilaterals will produce unpredictable results.

Answers

1. Check students' work.

2. 360

3. Check students' work. The sum of the measures of the exterior angles of a quadrilateral is 360.

4. The sum of the exterior angle measures of a pentagon is 360.

Angle Bisectors in Triangles I

For Use With Lesson 4-5

FILES NEEDED: Cabri® Jr.

AppVar: **GL45A**

Given: In GL45A, $\overline{AT}$ bisects $\angle BAC$.

Explore: angle bisectors in triangles

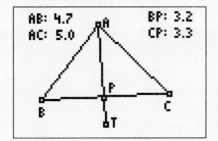

1. Drag point *A*, *B*, or *C*. Find four different isosceles triangles with *AB* = *AC*. For each triangle, record the lengths *BP* and *CP* in the table below.

BP				
CP				

2. Study the data in the table. Complete this conjecture about how lengths *BP* and *CP* are related.

   If the bisector of the vertex $\angle A$ of isosceles $\triangle ABC$ intersects the base $\overline{BC}$ in point *P*, then *BP* = __?__ .

3. Generalize your conjecture from Question 2.

   The bisector of the vertex angle of an isosceles triangle __?__ the base of the triangle.

4. Install screen-angle measures for $\angle BPA$ and $\angle CPA$. Drag point *A*, *B*, or *C*. Find four different isosceles triangles with *AB* = *AC*. For each triangle, record *m*$\angle BPA$ and *m*$\angle CPA$ in the table below.

m∠BPA				
m∠CPA				

5. Study the data in the table. Complete this conjecture about $\angle BPA$ and $\angle CPA$.

   If the bisector of the vertex $\angle A$ of isosceles $\triangle ABC$ intersects the base $\overline{BC}$ in point *P*, then $\angle BPA$ and $\angle CPA$ __?__ .

6. Generalize your conjecture from Question 5.

   The bisector of the vertex angle of an isosceles triangle __?__ the base of the triangle.

Extension

7. Combine your conjectures from Questions 3 and 6 into one statement.

8. Explain how to use **GL45A** to demonstrate the Isosceles Triangle Theorem.

Angle Bisectors in Triangles I

Activity Objective

Students use Cabri® Jr. to explore angle bisectors of isosceles triangles.

Correlation to Text

- Lesson 4-5: Isosceles and Equilateral Triangles

Time

- 15–20 minutes

Materials/Software

- App: Cabri® Jr.
- AppVar: GL45A
- Activity worksheet

Skills Needed

- drag an object
- install a measure

Classroom Management

- Students can work individually or in pairs depending on the number of calculators available.
- Use TI Connect™ software, TI-GRAPH LINK™ software, the TI-Navigator™ system, or unit-to-unit links to transfer **GL45A** to each calculator.

Notes

- In F1, select **Open** and then press `ENTER` to see the AppVar list.
- Students can drag only points A, B, and C. Points P and T are not draggable.
- Depending on the orientation of the triangle, it may not always be possible to match the lengths AB and AC exactly. Students can use values within one tenth of each other, or move B or C to reorient the base.

Answers

1. Check students' work.
2. CP
3. bisects
4. Check students' work.
5. are right angles
6. is perpendicular to
7. The bisector of the vertex angle of an isosceles triangle is the perpendicular bisector of the base of the triangle.
8. Answers may vary. Sample: Install screen-angle measures for $\angle B$ and $\angle C$. Find four different isosceles triangles with $AB = AC$. Record and study $m\angle B$ and $m\angle C$.

Segment Bisectors in Triangles

For Use With Lesson 4-5

FILES NEEDED: Cabri® Jr.
AppVar: **GL45B**

Given: In GL45B, point *D* bisects
side $\overline{AC}$ of △*ABC*.

Explore: segment bisectors in triangles

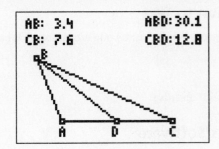

AB: 3.4   ABD: 30.1
CB: 7.6   CBD: 12.8

1. Drag point *A*, *B*, or *C*. Find four different
isosceles triangles with *AB* = *CB*. For each
triangle, record the angle measures indicated
in the table below.

$m\angle ABD$				
$m\angle CBFD$				

2. Study the data in the table. Complete the following conjecture.

   If point *D* bisects the base $\overline{AC}$ of isosceles △*ABC*, then $\overline{BD}$ __?__ .

3. Drag point *A*, *B*, or *C* to get *AB* = *CB* and $m\angle ABD$ as close to 45
as you can make it. What kind of triangle is △*ABC*? Explain.

Extension

Make $\overline{AC}$ horizontal. Replace the screen measures
AB and *CB* with *DB* and *DC* as shown at right.

DB: ABD: 30
DC: CBD: 60.4

4. Drag point *B* so that $\angle ABD$ and $\angle CBD$ are
complementary. What kind of triangle is △*ABC*?
Explain.

5. Drag point *B* so that $\angle ABD$ and $\angle CBD$ are
complementary in four different locations. In each
location, what do you observe about *DB* and *DC*?

6. Complete the following conjecture.

   In right △*ABC* with right angle *B*, length *DB* = __?__ .

7. Generalize your conjecture from Question 6.

   In a right triangle, the midpoint of the hypotenuse is __?__ .

Segment Bisectors in Triangles

Activity Objective

Students use Cabri® Jr. to explore medians in isosceles triangles.

Correlation to Text

- Lesson 4-5: Isosceles and Equilateral Triangles

Time

- 15–20 minutes

Materials/Software

- App: Cabri® Jr.
- AppVar: **GL45B**
- Activity worksheet

Skills Needed

- drag an object

Classroom Management

- Students can work individually or in pairs depending on the number of calculators available.
- Use TI Connect™ software, TI-GRAPH LINK™ software, the TI-Navigator™ system, or unit-to-unit links to transfer **GL45B** to each calculator.

Notes

- If students cannot match the lengths AB and CB exactly, suggest that they move point A or C to reorient the base.
- You may wish to introduce the term *median* with this Activity.

Answers

1. Check students' work.

2. bisects $\angle ABC$

3. Right isosceles triangle; Since $AB = CB$, it is isosceles. Since $m\angle ABD = 45, m\angle CBD = 45$ and $m\angle ABC = 90$, so $\triangle ABC$ is a right triangle.

4. Right triangle; $m\angle ABD + m\angle CBD = 90°$, so $\angle ABC$ is a right angle.

5. They are equal.

6. $\frac{1}{2}$ the length of the hypotenuse

7. equidistant from the three vertices

Triangle Midsegments

For Use With Lesson 5-1

FILES NEEDED: Cabri® Jr.
AppVar: **GL51**

Given: In GL51, △*ABC* has sides $\overline{AB}$ and $\overline{BC}$ with midpoints *D* and *E*, respectively.

Explore: properties of a midsegment of a triangle

1. Drag point *A* to different locations. Collect data for the first three blank columns of the table below.

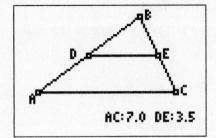

AC:7.0 DE:3.5

2. Drag point *C* to different locations. Collect data for the last three columns of the table.

Length *DE*						
Length *AC*						

3. Study the data in the table. Complete this conjecture about how lengths *DE* and *AC* are related.

   If *D* and *E* are midpoints of $\overline{AB}$ and $\overline{BC}$ in △*ABC*, then *DE* = __?__.

4. Generalize your conjecture from Question 3.

   The length of a midsegment of a triangle is __?__.

Install the slope of $\overline{DE}$ beside $\overline{DE}$. Install the slope of $\overline{AC}$ beside $\overline{AC}$.

5. Drag point *A* to three different locations. Then drag point *C* to three different locations. For each location, collect data for the table below.

Slope of $\overline{DE}$						
Slope of $\overline{AC}$						

6. Study the data in the table. Make a conjecture about how the slopes of a midsegment of a triangle and the corresponding base are related.

Extension

7. Construct the midpoint of $\overline{AC}$ and segments $\overline{DF}$ and $\overline{FE}$ to complete △*DEF*. Make a conjecture about how the perimeters of △*DEF* and △*ABC* are related.

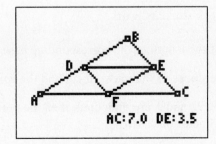

AC:7.0 DE:3.5

8. Install the two perimeters on the screen. Drag vertices to check your conjecture.

Triangle Midsegments

Activity Objective

Students use Cabri® Jr. to explore properties of triangle midsegments.

Correlation to Text

- Lesson 5-1: Midsegments of Triangles

Time

- 20–30 minutes

Materials/Software

- App: Cabri® Jr.
- AppVar: **GL51**
- Activity worksheet

Skills Needed

- drag an object
- construct a midpoint
- install a measure
- draw a segment

Classroom Management

- Students can work individually or in pairs depending on the number of calculators available.
- Use TI Connect™ software, TI-GRAPH LINK™ software, the TI-Navigator™ system, or unit-to-unit links to transfer **GL51** to each calculator.

Notes

- Students cannot drag points D and E because D and E are constructed as the midpoints of segments $\overline{AB}$ and $\overline{BC}$.
- Dragging point B will not cause changes in the lengths nor the slopes of $\overline{DE}$ or $\overline{AC}$. Students can investigate this property of $\triangle ABC$ as well.

Answers

1–2. Check students' work.

3. $\frac{1}{2}AC$

4. half the length of the corresponding base

5. Check students' work.

6. The slopes of the midsegment and the corresponding base are equal.

7. If D, E, and F are midpoints, then the perimeter of $\triangle DEF$ is half the perimeter of $\triangle ABC$.

8. Check students' work.

Perpendicular Bisectors in Triangles   For Use With Lesson 5-3

FILES NEEDED: Cabri® Jr.
AppVar: **GL53**

Given: in GL53, $\triangle ABC$

Explore: perpendicular bisectors in triangles

Step 1: For $\triangle ABC$, construct the perpendicular bisector of sides $\overline{AB}$ and $\overline{AC}$.

Step 2: Construct the point at the intersection of the two perpendicular bisectors. Name it P.

Step 3: Construct a circle centered at P. For the radius, join P to one vertex of the triangle.

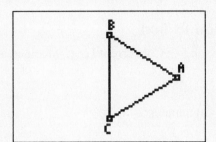

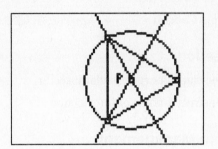

1. Why can you conclude that $PA = PB = PC$?

2. What can you conclude about the circle you drew in Step 3?

3. The circle is the *circumcircle* of the triangle and point P is the *circumcenter*. Explain why *circumcircle* is a fitting name for this circle.

4. Drag vertex A toward side $\overline{BC}$ until the circumcenter lies on $\overline{BC}$. Estimate $m\angle BAC$.

5. Drag vertex A closer to $\overline{BC}$. Does the circumcenter remain within the triangle? Does the circle still pass through all three vertices? Justify your answer.

6. Describe the type of triangle to complete each conjecture.

If the circumcenter is inside the triangle, the triangle is __?__ .
If the circumcenter is outside the triangle, the triangle is __?__ .

7. If your conjectures in Question 6 are true, what can you conclude about the triangle if the circumcenter lies on the triangle?

Extension

8. As vertex A gets very close to $\overline{BC}$, what happens to P? To the circumcircle?

9. If A lies on $\overline{BC}$, what happens to the perpendicular bisectors? To P? To the circle?

Animation Option

Animate vertex A and watch it pass back and forth through $\overline{BC}$.
Note how the perpendicular bisectors and the size of the circle change.

Perpendicular Bisectors in Triangles

Activity Objective

Students use Cabri® Jr. to explore properties of perpendicular bisectors of triangles.

Correlation to Text

- Lesson 5-3: Concurrent Lines, Medians, and Altitudes

Time

- 20–30 minutes

Materials/Software

- App: Cabri Jr.
- AppVar: **GL53**
- Activity worksheet

Skills Needed

- construct a perpendicular bisector
- construct a point of intersection
- construct a circle
- drag an object
- animate an object

Classroom Management

- Students can work individually or in pairs depending on the number of calculators available.
- Use TI Connect™ software, TI-GRAPH LINK™ software, the TI-Navigator™ system, or unit-to-unit links to transfer **GL53** to each calculator.

Notes

- $\triangle ABC$ is constructed so that point A can be animated.

Error Prevention

- When students attach the radius to one of the vertices of $\triangle ABC$, they need to be sure the vertex is flashing before they press ENTER .

Answers

1. A point on the perpendicular bisector of a segment is equidistant from the endpoints.

2. It contains all three vertices of the triangle.   3.   *circum-* (Latin) means around.

4. $m\angle BAC \approx 90°$.   5.   no; yes, same as Question 1

6. acute; obtuse   7.   The triangle is a right triangle.

8. P gets farther and farther away from $\overline{BC}$. The circumcircle becomes larger and larger.

9. They become parallel through P at infinity and the circle becomes a line.

Inequalities in Triangles

For Use With Lesson 5-5

FILES NEEDED: Cabri® Jr.

AppVar: GL55

Given: in GL55, △ABC

Explore: the side lengths and angle measures
of triangles

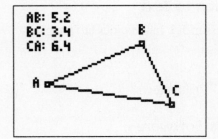

AB: 5.2
BC: 3.4
CA: 6.4

1. Drag any vertex of triangle △ABC to form
four different triangles. Record lengths
AB, BC, and CA for each triangle in the
table below.

Length AB				
Length BC				
Length CA				
Sum of two smallest lengths				

2. In each column of the table, ring the greatest length. Write the sum
of the two smallest lengths in the bottom row.

3. Study the data in the table. Make a conjecture about an inequality
relationship between the sum of the lengths of the two shorter sides
of a triangle and the length of the longest side.

4. Generalize your conjecture from Question 3 to a conjecture about the
sum of the lengths of *any* two sides of a triangle and the length of the
third side.

5. Assume that the conjecture from Question 3 is true. Then give a
convincing argument that your new conjecture from Question 4 is
true, or find a counterexample to show that it is false.

Extension

6. Install the screen-angle measures for ∠A, ∠B, and ∠C. Drag any
vertex of triangle △ABC to form four different triangles. In the table
below, record m∠A, m∠B, and, m∠C for each triangle, along with
the length of the side opposite each angle.

m∠A, length BC							
m∠B, length CA							
m∠C, length AB							

7. For each triangle ring the greatest angle measure and greatest length. Box
the smallest angle measure and smallest length. Make a conjecture.

Inequalities in Triangles

Activity Objective

Students use Cabri® Jr. to explore inequalities in triangles.

Correlation to Text

- Lesson 5-5: Inequalities in Triangles

Time

- 20–30 minutes

Materials/Software

- App: Cabri Jr.
- AppVar: GL55
- Activity worksheet

Skills Needed

- install a measure
- drag an object

Classroom Management

- Students can work individually or in pairs depending on the number of calculators available.
- Use TI Connect™ software, TI-GRAPH LINK™ software, the TI-Navigator™ system, or unit-to-unit links to transfer **GL55** to each calculator.

Error Prevention

- Some students may form an equilateral triangle. In this case, tell them that they can consider any side to be the longest side.
- It is possible to form triangles for which the sum of the lengths of two sides of the triangle appear to be *equal to* the length of the third side. This is due to the limited precision of the screen measurements.

Answers

1–2, 6. Check students' work.

3. The sum of the lengths of the two shorter sides is greater than the length of the longest side.

4. The sum of the lengths of any two sides of a triangle is greater than the length of the third side.

5. Sample: Question 4 conjecture must be true. The sum for any two sides is no less than the sum for the two shorter sides. Also, any side is no longer than the longest side.

7. The largest angle and longest side are opposite each other as are the smallest angle and shortest side.

Area of a Triangle

For Use With Lesson 7-1

FILES NEEDED: Cabri® Jr.
AppVars: **GL71A, GL71B**

Given: In **GL71A**, $\overleftrightarrow{DE} \parallel \overleftrightarrow{AC}$ and $\overline{BP} \perp \overleftrightarrow{AC}$.
$\triangle ABC$ has base length AC and height BP.

Explore: area of $\triangle ABC$

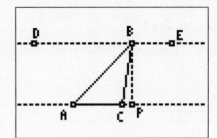

1. Install the screen measures BP and area of $\triangle ABC$. Predict what will happen to each screen measure as you drag point B along $\overleftrightarrow{DE}$.

2. Justify each prediction. Then test your predictions by dragging B along $\overleftrightarrow{DE}$.

Before doing Question 2, save your **GL71A** from Question 1 as **PIC1**.

In **GL71B** at the right, $\triangle ABC$ is the same triangle as the one shown above. In this case, however, $\overleftrightarrow{EF} \parallel \overline{AB}$.

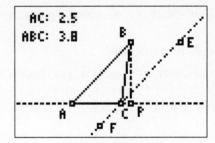

3. Predict what will happen to the screen measures AC and area of $\triangle ABC$ as you drag C along $\overleftrightarrow{EF}$.

4. Justify each prediction. Then test your predictions by dragging C along $\overleftrightarrow{EF}$.

5. For each of three locations of C, predict the value of BP. Then test your predictions by installing the screen measure BP. If your predictions are correct, explain why.

Extension

Recall the screen that you saved as **PIC1**. Replace the screen measures for BP with the measures for AB and BC. Also, install the screen measure for the perimeter of $\triangle ABC$. Note that you now have four measures on the screen.

6. Drag point B along $\overleftrightarrow{DE}$. Describe $\triangle ABC$ for large values of the perimeter and for small values of the perimeter.

7. Drag B to find the smallest value of the perimeter. What type of triangle does $\triangle ABC$ appear to be? Give a convincing argument why $\triangle ABC$ must be this type of triangle.

Area of a Triangle

Activity Objective

Students use Cabri® Jr. to explore the relationship between the base and height and the area of a triangle.

Correlation to Text

- Lesson 7-1: Areas of Parallelograms and Triangles

Time

- 15–20 minutes

Materials/Software

- App: Cabri® Jr.
- AppVars: **GL71A, GL71B**
- Activity worksheet

Skills Needed

- drag an object
- install a measure

Classroom Management

- Use TI Connect™ software, TI-GRAPH LINK™ software, the TI-Navigator™ system, or unit-to-unit links to transfer **GL71A** and **GL71B** to each calculator.

Notes

- Students should notice that the initial area of $\triangle ABC$ is the same in **GL71A** and **GL71B**.

Answers

1. The height and the area will not change.
2. $\overleftrightarrow{DE}$ and $\overleftrightarrow{AC}$ are parallel, so BP will not change. The area does not change because it depends on base and height, which do not change.
3. AC will change. The area will stay the same.
4. AC increases as C moves away from A toward E. AC decreases as C moves closer to A in the direction of F. Area stays the same because 1) base $\overline{AB}$ does not change and 2) the height to $\overline{AB}$ stays the same as parallel lines remain a constant distance apart.
5. Check students' work. $BP = \frac{2 \cdot \text{Area } \triangle ABC}{AC}$ (both numerator and denominator shown on screen).
6. $\triangle ABC$ is obtuse for large perimeters and acute for small perimeters.
7. Isosceles; Answers may vary. Sample: For every non-isosceles triangle, there is a second triangle congruent to it. These two triangles determine two locations of B. The triangle for each location of B between these two points has a smaller perimeter. Thus the smallest perimeter must occur where $BA = BC$.

Triangles and Circles

| **FILES NEEDED:** Cabri® Jr. |
| AppVars: **GL72A, GL72B** |

Given: In GL72A, $\triangle ABC$ has $\overline{AB}$ as a diameter of
the circle and point C on the circle.

Explore: $\triangle ABC$

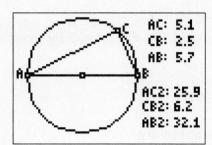

1. Drag point C to four different locations on
the circle. (See Animation Option below.)
Record the values of AC^2, CB^2, and AB^2 in
the table below.

AC^2				
CB^2				
AB^2				

2. Study the table. How are AC^2, CB^2, and AB^2 related?

3. Recall the Converse of the Pythagorean Theorem. Use it to help you
complete the following conjecture.

    If $\overline{AB}$ is the diameter of a circle and point C lies on the circle, then
$\triangle ABC$ is   ? .

4. Generalize your conjecture from Question 3 to a conjecture about a triangle
inscribed in a circle with one of its sides a diameter of the circle.

Extension

In **GL72B**, point P is the center of the circle. $\triangle ABC$
has point C on the circle and $\overline{AB}$ as a diameter.

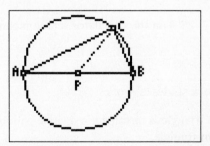

5. Install the screen measures of $\angle ACP$ and
$\angle BCP$. Drag point C around the circle. What
do you notice about $m\angle ACP$ and $m\angle BCP$?

6. What is true about $\overline{PA}$, $\overline{PB}$, and $\overline{PC}$? What
kind of triangles are $\triangle APC$ and $\triangle BPC$?

7. Write a proof of your conjecture in Question 3.
(*Hint:* Use your answers from Question 6.)

Animation Option

In Question 1, animate point C and stop it at different locations to collect
your data.

Triangles and Circles

Activity Objective

Students use Cabri® Jr. to explore properties of triangles inscribed in circles.

Correlation to Text

- Lesson 7-2: The Pythagorean Theorem and Its Converse

Time

- 20–30 minutes

Materials/Software

- App: Cabri® Jr.
- AppVar: GL72A, GL72B
- Activity worksheet

Skills Needed

- drag an object
- install a measure

Classroom Management

- Students can work individually or in pairs depending on the number of calculators available.
- Use TI Connect™ software, TI-GRAPH LINK™ software, the TI-Navigator™ system, or unit-to-unit links to transfer GL72A and GL72B to each calculator.
- For Question 5, suggest that students collect data in a table.

Notes

- AC2: 25.9 on the calculator screen means "$AC^2 = 25.9$."

Answers

1. Check students' work.
2. $AC^2 + CB^2 = AB^2$
3. a right triangle

4. If a triangle is inscribed in a circle with one of its sides a diameter, then it is a right triangle.

5. The sum of their measures is about 90.
6. They are congruent; isosceles.

7. Since $\triangle APC$ and $\triangle BPC$ are isosceles, $m\angle A = m\angle ACP$ and $m\angle B = m\angle BCP$. $m\angle A + m\angle B + m\angle ACB = 180$, so $m\angle ACP + m\angle BCP + m\angle ACB = 180$. But $m\angle ACP + m\angle BCP = m\angle ACB$, so $m\angle ACB + m\angle ACB = 180$, or $2\, m\angle ACB = 180$. Thus, $m\angle ACB = 90$ and $\triangle ABC$ is a right triangle.

Areas of Rhombuses and Kites

For Use With Lesson 7-4

FILES NEEDED: Cabri® Jr.
AppVars: **GL74A, GL74B**

Given: In **GL74A**, $\overline{RHMB}$ is a rhombus with
diagonals $\overline{RM}$ and $\overline{HB}$.

Explore: the area of a rhombus

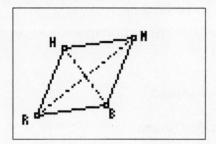

1. Install the screen measures for *RM, HB*, and
   the area of rhombus *RHMB*. Drag point *H*
   or *B*. For four different rhombuses, record
   each measure in the table below.

RM				
HB				
Area				

2. Study the data in the table. Make a conjecture that relates the area
   of rhombus *RHMB* to the lengths of diagonals $\overline{RM}$ and $\overline{HB}$.

3. Reword your conjecture from Question 2 to relate the area of *any*
   rhombus to the lengths of its diagonals.

In **GL74B**, *KITE* is a kite with diagonals $\overline{KT}$ and $\overline{IE}$.

4. Install the screen measures for *KT, IE*, and
   the area of *KITE*. Drag point *K, I,* or *T*. For
   four different kites, record each measure in
   the table below.

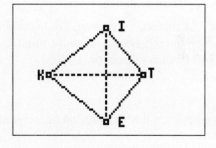

KT				
IE				
Area				

5. Study the data in the table. Make a conjecture that relates the area
   of any kite to the lengths of its diagonals.

Extension

6. A square is a rhombus. Reword your conjecture from Question 3 to
   make a conjecture about the area of a square.

7. A rectangle has congruent diagonals, just like a square. In your
   conjecture from Question 6, replace "square" with "rectangle" to form
   a new conjecture. Is this conjecture true? Give a convincing argument.

8. Prove that your conjectures from Questions 3 and 5 are true.

Areas of Rhombuses and Kites

Activity Objective

Students use Cabri® Jr. to explore areas of rhombuses and kites.

Correlation to Text

- Lesson 7-4: Areas of Trapezoids, Rhombuses, and Kites

Time

- 20–30 minutes

Materials/Software

- App: Cabri® Jr.
- AppVar: **GL74A, GL74B**
- Activity worksheet

Skills Needed

- install a measure
- drag an object

Classroom Management

- Students can work individually or in pairs depending on the number of calculators available.
- Use TI Connect™ software, TI-GRAPH LINK™ software, the TI-Navigator™ system, or unit-to-unit links to transfer **GL74A** and **GL74B** to each calculator.

Notes

- Diagonals are dashed lines on the screen.

Answers

1. Check students' work. 2. Area of $RHMB = \frac{1}{2}(RM)(HB)$

3. The area of a rhombus is one half the product of the lengths of its diagonals.

4. Check students' work. 5. The area of a kite is one half the product of the lengths of its diagonals.

6. The area of a square is one half the square of the length of a diagonal.

7. The area of a rectangle is half the square of the length of a diagonal. False. You can rotate the diagonals to form a variety of rectangles that have different areas.

8. Proofs may vary. Sample (referring to rhombus $RHMB$ on the Activity page with diagonals intersecting at point P): Area $RHMB$ = Area $\triangle RHM$ + Area $\triangle MBR$ = $\frac{1}{2}(RM)(HP) + \frac{1}{2}(RM)(PB) = \frac{1}{2}(RM)(HP + PB) = \frac{1}{2}(RM)(HB)$.

Parallel Segments in Triangles

For Use With Lesson 8-5

FILES NEEDED: Cabri® Jr.
AppVar: **GL85A**

Given: In GL85A, $\overline{DE}$ is parallel to side $\overline{AC}$ of $\triangle ABC$ with point D on $\overline{AB}$ and point E on $\overline{BC}$.

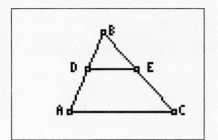

Explore: the ratios of the lengths of the divided sides

1. Install lengths AD, DB, CE, and EB on your screen. Drag point D to four different locations on $\overline{AB}$. For each location record the four lengths in the table below.

Length AD				
Length DB				
Length CE				
Length EB				
$\dfrac{AD}{DB}$				
$\dfrac{CE}{EB}$				

2. For each column in the table, find the ratios $\frac{AD}{DB}$ and $\frac{CE}{EB}$ to the nearest tenth. Record the values in the last two rows of the table.

3. Study the data in the table. Complete the following conjecture about the relationship between $\frac{AD}{DB}$ and $\frac{CE}{EB}$.

   If $\overline{DE}$ is parallel to side $\overline{AC}$ of $\triangle ABC$ with D on $\overline{AB}$ and E on $\overline{BC}$, then __?__.

4. Generalize your conjecture from Question 3.

   If a line is parallel to one side of a triangle and intersects the other two sides, then __?__.

Extension

5. Drag point C until $\triangle ABC$ is an isosceles triangle with $AB = CB$. What kind of triangle is $\triangle DBE$? Explain your answer.

6. Draw $\overline{GH}$ parallel to $\overline{AC}$ of $\triangle ABC$ with point G on $\overline{AD}$ and point H on $\overline{EC}$. Make a conjecture about the ratio $AG:GD:DB$.

Parallel Segments in Triangles

Activity Objective

Students use Cabri® Jr. to explore the properties of parallel segments in triangles.

Correlation to Text

- Lesson 8-5: Proportions in Triangles

Time

- 20–30 minutes

Materials/Software

- App: Cabri® Jr.
- AppVar: GL85A
- Activity worksheet

Skills Needed

- install a measure
- drag an object

Classroom Management

- Students can work individually or in pairs depending on the number of calculators available.
- Use TI Connect™ software, TI-GRAPH LINK™ software, the TI-Navigator™ system, or unit-to-unit links to transfer **GL85A** to each calculator.

Answers

1-2. Check students' work.

3. $\dfrac{AD}{DB} = \dfrac{CE}{EB}$

4. the line divides the two sides proportionally

5. $\triangle DBE$ is isosceles; If $\dfrac{AD}{DB} = \dfrac{CE}{EB}$, then $\dfrac{AD + DB}{DB} = \dfrac{CE + EB}{EB}$, or $\dfrac{AB}{DB} = \dfrac{CB}{EB}$. When $AB = CB$, it follows that $DB = EB$, so $\triangle DBE$ is isosceles.

6. $AG : GD : DB = CH : HE : EB$

Angle Bisectors in Triangles II

For Use With Lesson 8-5

FILES NEEDED: Cabri® Jr.

AppVar: **GL85B**

Given: In GL85B, $\overleftrightarrow{AD}$ bisects $\angle CAB$ of $\triangle ABC$ and intersects side $\overline{CB}$ in point D.

Explore: the ratio of the lengths of the divided side

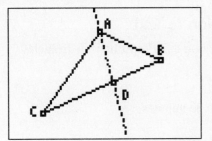

1. Install lengths $CA, AB, CD,$ and DB on your screen. Drag point B to form four different triangles. For each triangle record the four lengths in the table below.

Length CA				
Length AB				
Length CD				
Length DB				
$\frac{CA}{AB}$				
$\frac{CD}{DB}$				

2. For each column in the table, find the ratios $\frac{CA}{AB}$ and $\frac{CD}{DB}$ to the nearest tenth. Record the values in the last two rows of the table.

3. Study the data in the table. Complete the following conjecture about the relationship between $\frac{CD}{DB}$ and $\frac{CA}{AB}$.

   If $\overleftrightarrow{AD}$ bisects $\angle CAB$ of $\triangle ABC$ and intersects side $\overline{CB}$ in point D, then __?__.

4. Generalize your conjecture from Question 3.

   A line that bisects an angle of a triangle divides the side opposite that angle into two segments whose lengths are proportional to __?__.

Extension

5. Drag point B to make $CD = DB$. What kind of triangle is $\triangle ABC$? Explain your answer.

6. Explain how, without measuring any angle, you could locate a point E on $\overline{AC}$ so that $\overleftrightarrow{BE}$ bisects $\angle ABC$.

Angle Bisectors in Triangles II

Activity Objective

Students use Cabri® Jr. to explore the properties of angles bisectors in triangles.

Correlation to Text

- Lesson 8-5: Proportions in Triangles

Time

- 20–30 minutes

Materials/Software

- App: Cabri® Jr.
- AppVar: **GL85B**
- Activity worksheet

Skills Needed

- install a measure
- drag an object

Classroom Management

- Students can work individually or in pairs depending on the number of calculators available.
- Use TI Connect™ software, TI-GRAPH LINK™ software, the TI-Navigator™ system, or unit-to-unit links to transfer **GL85B** to each calculator.

Answers

1-2. Check students' work.

3. $\frac{CD}{DB} = \frac{CA}{AB}$

4. the lengths of the sides of the angle

5. isosceles; If $CD = DB$, then $\frac{CA}{AB} = 1$, and $CA = AB$.

6. If $\overleftrightarrow{BE}$ bisects $\angle ABC$, $\frac{AE}{EC}$ must equal $\frac{BA}{BC}$. Install lengths AE, EC, BA, and BC. Locate E so that $AE = EC \cdot \frac{BA}{BC}$. Then $\frac{AE}{EC} = \frac{BA}{BC}$.

Perimeters and Areas of Squares

For Use With Lesson 8-6

> **FILES NEEDED:** Cabri® Jr.
> AppVar: **GL86**

Given: In **GL86**, *ABCD* and *AEFG* are squares.

Explore: the ratios of side lengths, perimeters, and areas of squares

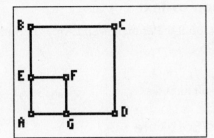

1. On your screen, install the lengths *AB* and *AE*, and the perimeters and areas of *ABCD* and *AEFG*. Drag points *D* and *G* to form four different pairs of squares. Record all six measures for each pair in the table below.

Length *AB*				
Length *AE*				
Perimeter of *ABCD*				
Perimeter of *AEFG*				
Area of *ABCD*				
Area of *AEFG*				

2. Use data from the table above. For each column, find and record the ratios shown in the table below to the nearest tenth.

$\dfrac{AB}{AE}$				
$\dfrac{\text{Perimeter of } ABCD}{\text{Perimeter of } AEFG}$				
$\dfrac{(AB)^2}{(AE)^2}$				
$\dfrac{\text{Area of } ABCD}{\text{Area of } AEFG}$				

3. Study the data in the table. Make two conjectures about the ratios shown in the table.

4. Generalize your conjectures from Question 3 to apply to all squares. (*Hint:* The perimeters of any two squares are proportional to . . .)

Animation Option

Animate points *D* and *G* to form the different squares.

Perimeters and Areas of Squares

Activity Objective

Students use Cabri® Jr. to explore the perimeters and areas of squares.

Correlation to Text

- Lesson 8-6: Perimeters and Areas of Similar Figures

Time

- 20–30 minutes

Materials/Software

- App: Cabri® Jr.
- AppVar: **GL86**
- Activity worksheet

Skills Needed

- install a measure
- drag an object

Classroom Management

- Students can work individually or in pairs depending on the number of calculators available.
- Use TI Connect™ software, TI-GRAPH LINK™ software, the TI-Navigator™ system, or unit-to-unit links to transfer **GL86** to each calculator.

Notes

- Ask students if they think the same relationships will apply to rectangles or triangles. Have them explain their answers.

Answers

1-2. Check students' work.

3. $\dfrac{AB}{AE} = \dfrac{\text{Perimeter of } ABCD}{\text{Perimeter of } AEFG}.$

$\dfrac{(AB)^2}{(AE)^2} = \dfrac{\text{Area of } ABCD}{\text{Area of } AEFG}.$

4. The perimeters of two squares are proportional to the lengths of their sides. The areas of two squares are proportional to the squares of the lengths of their sides.

Inscribed Angles

For Use With Lesson 11-3

FILES NEEDED: Cabri® Jr.
AppVars: **GL113A, GL113B**

Given: In GL113A, points *B, C, D* and *E*, are on a
circle with center *A*. $\overline{DE}$ (only endpoints
shown) is a diameter of the circle.

Explore: inscribed angles

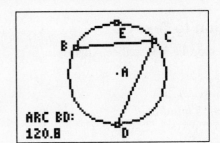

ARC BD:
120.8

1 Install the screen measure of ∠*BCD*.

2. Drag both points *B* and *C* along the circle to
form four different angles *BCD*. Keep *B* to
the left and *C* to the right of diameter $\overline{DE}$.
Record the measures listed in the table below.

$m\angle BCD$				
$m\overarc{BD}$				

3. Study the data in the table. Make a conjecture about the relationship
between $m\angle BCD$ and $m\overarc{BD}$.

4. Generalize your conjecture from Question 3 to a conjecture about
the measure of any inscribed angle and its intercepted arc.

5. Predict what will happen if you drag point *C* along the circle without
moving *B*? Justify your prediction. Then test it by dragging *C*.

6. $\overarc{BD}$ is intercepted by both inscribed ∠*BCD* and central angle
∠*BAD*. Make a conjecture relating the measures of an inscribed
angle and a central angle that intercept the same arc. Install
$m\angle BAD$ and check your conjecture.

Extension

Open GL113B. $\overline{RT}$ is a diameter of the circle and *P*
is a point on the circle.

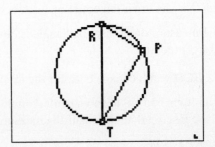

7. Install the screen measure of ∠*RPT*.
Drag point *P*. (See Animation Option
below.) What do you observe?

8. Make a conjecture about a triangle inscribed
in a circle and with one side a diameter.

Animation Option

Animate point *P* along the circle.

Inscribed Angles

Activity Objective

Students use Cabri® Jr. to explore the relationship between inscribed angles and their intercepted arcs.

Correlation to Text

- Lesson 11-3: Inscribed Angles

Time

- 10–15 minutes

Materials/Software

- App: Cabri® Jr.
- AppVars: **GL113A, GL113B**
- Activity worksheet

Skills Needed

- install a measure
- drag an object
- animate an object

Classroom Management

- Students can work individually or in pairs depending on the number of calculators available.
- Use TI Connect™ software, TI-GRAPH LINK™ software, the TI-Navigator™ system, or unit-to-unit links to transfer AppVars **GL113A** and **GL113B** to each calculator.

Error Prevention

- Make sure students do not form intercepted arcs greater than 180°. Cabri Jr. will not generate angle measures greater than 180.

Answers

1–2. Check students' work.

3. If $\overset{\frown}{BD}$ is the arc intercepted by inscribed $\angle BCD$, then $m\angle BCD = \frac{1}{2}m\overset{\frown}{BD}$.

4. The measure of an inscribed angle is equal to half the measure of its intercepted arc.

5. $m\angle BCD$ won't change because the intercepted arc does not change.

6. If an inscribed angle and a central angle intercept the same arc, the measure of the inscribed angle is half the measure of the central angle.

7. $m\angle RPT = 90$

8. A triangle inscribed in a circle with one side a diameter is a right triangle.

Reflections

FILE NEEDED: Cabri® Jr.

---

1. Follow the steps to draw, animate, and demonstrate a dynamic image and its equally-dynamic reflection image.

   Step 1: Draw a vertical line.

   Step 2: Draw a circle so that the line is about halfway between the center and the radius point. See the screen at the right.

   Step 3: Construct a triangle with each vertex on the circle. Do not place a vertex on the line.

   Step 4: Use **Reflection** in **F4** to reflect the triangle across the line. See the second screen at the right.

   Step 5: Hide the circle, its center and radius points, and the vertical line and its defining points.

   Step 6: Choose one vertex on the original triangle. Animate it. After you see how the triangle and its reflection change, animate another vertex. Finally animate the third vertex.

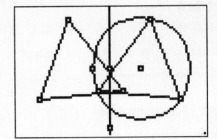

2. Stop the animation at a place of your choosing. Sketch the symmetric figure you see. Draw the line of symmetry in your sketch.

Extension

3. To make the animation more interesting, follow Steps 7 and 8.

   Step 7: Construct a segment between each vertex and its reflection.

   Step 8: Animate the vertices, one at a time, until all three are moving.

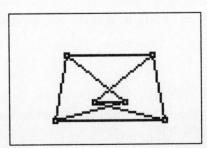

4. How is the vertical line from Step 1 related to the three segments you constructed in Step 7? Explain.

5. How are the three segments you constructed in Step 7 related to each other? Explain.

Reflections

Activity Objective

Students use Cabri® Jr. to explore reflected images.

Correlation to Text

- Lesson 12-1: Reflections

Time

- 25–35 minutes

Materials/Software

- App: Cabri® Jr.
- Activity worksheet

Skills Needed

- draw a line
- animate a point
- reflect an object
- hide an object
- construct a triangle
- draw a circle
- construct a segment

Classroom Management

- Students can work individually or in pairs depending on the number of calculators available.

Notes

- The relative positions of the line and circle impacts the appearance of the construction. If the line sits on the edge of the circle, the animated points will meet but not cross over.
- Animate in **F1** activates one point at a time. Students can generate different images by varying the time between animating points and the activation sequence.
- Students who complete the activity quickly should try their own variations.

Answers

1-3. Check students' work.

4. It is the perpendicular bisector of each segment by the definition of reflection.

5. They are parallel. Lines perpendicular to the same line are parallel to each other.

Parallels and Perpendiculars

For Use With Lesson 2-2

FILES NEEDED: Transformation Graphing App
Program: A2L22

A2L22 graphs the linear equation or function $y = mx + b$ as Y1 = AX + B.

In this activity you will explore the relationships between the equation of a line and the slopes of lines parallel and perpendicular to its graph.

1. Run A2L22 to see a fixed line (two points marked) and line Y1 = AX + B with A = 0 and B = 5. From looking at the screen, how would you change A to make the two lines parallel?

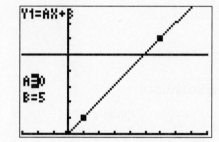

2. Change the value of A until the lines appear to be parallel. Record this value in the table below.

3. Change the value of A until the lines appear to be perpendicular. Record this value in the table.

4. Use **TRACE** to find the coordinates of the two marked points on the fixed line. Record these in the table. Then use the slope formula $m = \dfrac{y_2 - y_1}{x_2 - x_1}$ to fill in the last column.

	Slope of parallel line	Slope of perpendicular line	Coordinates of marked points	Slope of fixed line
Questions 2–4				
Question 5				
Question 6				

5. Switch from **Plot1** to **Plot2**. Repeat Questions 2–4 for the new fixed line.

6. Switch from **Plot2** to **Plot3**. Repeat Questions 2–4. (*Hint:* When you look for the perpendicular line, first change the value of B to −4.)

7. Make a conjecture about the slopes of parallel lines; about the slopes of perpendicular lines.

8. Test your conjectures. Let Y1 = 3X + 7. Write equations for Y2 and Y3 so that their graphs are parallel and perpendicular, respectively, to the graph of Y1. Graph the lines in a square window.

Extension

9. Write equations of a line parallel $2x + 5y = 7$ and of a line perpendicular to $2x + 5y = 7$.

Parallels and Perpendiculars

Activity Objective

Students use the Transformation Graphing App to explore the relationships between the equation of a line and the slopes of lines parallel and perpendicular to its graph.

Correlation to Text

- Lesson 2-2: Linear Equations

Time

- 20–25 minutes

Materials/Software

- Transformation Graphing App
- Program: **A2L22**
- Activity worksheet

Skills Needed

- change parameter values
- select and deselect plots

Notes

- Reminder: As noted on p. vi, each Activity page assumes that you activate the appropriate App at the start of the activity.
- Be certain that students understand which line is the graph of Y1 = AX + B.
- Remind students that they can enter parameter values A and B directly.
- Discuss with students how to deselect and select a plot in either the Y= or STAT PLOT screens.

Answers

1. Increase the value of A.

2–6. See table below.

	Slope of parallel line	Slope of perpendicular line	Coordinates of marked points	Slope of fixed line
Questions 2–4	1	−1	(1, 1) (6, 6)	1
Question 5	0.5	−2	(2, 1) (6, 3)	$\frac{1}{2}$
Question 6	−0.25	4	(0, 3) (4, 2) (8, 1)	$-\frac{1}{4}$

7. The slopes of parallel lines are equal; the slopes of perpendicular lines are opposite reciprocals of each other.

8. Check students' work. The parallel line must have slope 3. The perpendicular line must have slope $-\frac{1}{3}$.

9. Check students' work. The parallel line must have slope $-\frac{2}{5}$. The perpendicular line must have slope $\frac{5}{2}$.

Name _____ Class _____ Date _____

Visualizing Linear Models

FILES NEEDED: Transformation Graphing App
    Programs: **A2L24A, A2L24B, A2L24C**

The programs in this activity relate to Exercises 12, 20, and 21 in textbook Lesson 2-4. When you run each program, the startup screen shows the linear equation $y = mx + b$ graphed as $Y1 = AX + B$, and the startup values for A and B.

For each scatter plot, manipulate the line **Y1** to find the best trend line that you can to model the data. Write the linear equation and answer the related questions.

1. For text Exercise 12, run **A2L24A** and find a trend line to model the data. (*Hint:* Find a reasonable slope; then the *y*-intercept.) Use **ENTER** to change parameter values.

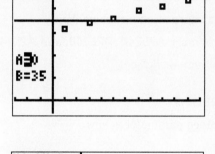

2. For your model, find the European equivalent of U.S. size 8.

3. Explain how you can use your model to find the U.S. equivalent of a European size.

4. For text Exercise 20, run **A2L24B** and find a trend line to model the data. Round the value for the slope to hundredths.

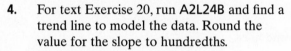

5. How much fat would you expect a 330-Calorie hamburger to have?

6. What is the meaning of the *y*-intercept? What value would you expect for it?

7. For text Exercise 21, which variable should be the independent variable?

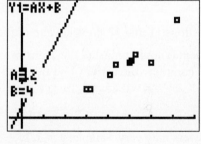

8. Run **A2L24C**. Find a trend line to model the data. Find A and B to tenths.

9. When the data were collected, the population of Oregon was approximately 3 million. Use your model to estimate how many licensed drivers there were in Oregon.

10. What is the meaning of the *y*-intercept? What value would you expect for it?

11. Which point represents Florida? Ignore that point and find your best model for the remaining data. How do your two models differ and why?

12. Use your second model to estimate the number of licensed drivers in Oregon. In which estimate, this one or the one in Exercise 9, would you have more confidence? Explain.

Visualizing Linear Models

Activity Objective

Students use the Transformation Graphing App to find a trend line to model data.

Correlation to Text

- Lesson 2-4: Using Linear Models

Time

- 20–25 minutes

Materials/Software

- Transformation Graphing App
- Programs: **A2L24A, A2L24B,** and **A2L24C**
- Activity worksheet

Skills Needed

- change parameter values

Notes

- Questions 11 and 12 show how an outlier affects trend lines.
- Students should uninstall the Transformation Graphing App when they complete the activity and then run **DEFAULT.**

Answers

1. Answers may vary. Sample: $y = 1.3x + 30$ 2. size 40

3. Answers may vary. Sample: Trace along the trend line and find the x-value (U.S. size) for a given y-value (European size).

4. Answers may vary. Sample: $y = 0.07x - 9$ 5. about 14 g

6. The y-intercept is the amount of fat if there were no Calories. It should be 0.

7. population   8. Answers may vary. Sample: $y = 0.8x - 0.5$ 9. 1.9 million

10. The y-intercept shows the number of licensed drivers you would expect if the state had population zero. You would expect this value to be 0.

11. The point at the far upper right of the screen. Answers may vary. Sample: $y = 0.7x$. The Florida data increase the slope of the trend line.

12. 2.1 million; check students' work.

All rights reserved.

© Pearson Education, Inc., publishing as Pearson Prentice Hall

96   *Algebra 2* Lesson 2-4 Teacher Notes   **TI-83/84 Plus Activities**

Absolute Value Translations I

For Use With Lesson 2-5

FILES NEEDED: Transformation Graphing App
Program: A2L25

A2L25 graphs the absolute value function $y = |mx + b| + c$ as
Y1 = abs(AX + B) + C. In this activity you will study the relationship
between the vertex of a graph and the values of m, b, and c.

1. Run A2L25. The startup graph has A = 1, B = 0,
   and C = 0. Write the equation for this absolute
   value function. What are the coordinates of
   its vertex?

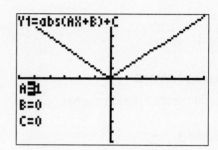

2. Vary the value of A. What effect does changing
   A have on the vertex? On the graph?

3. Set A = 1 and B = 0, and vary the value of C.
   What effect does changing C have on
   the vertex?

4. Set A = 1 and C = 0, and vary the value of B. What effect does
   changing B have on the vertex?

5. When A = 1, predict the coordinates of the vertex for each pair of B
   and C values given below. Test your predictions.

   B = 2, C = 3   B = 4, C = −2   B = −1, C = 3   B = −4, C = −1

6. Set A = 2, B = 0, and C = 0. What is the effect
   on the graph for changing the value of C?
   Of B?

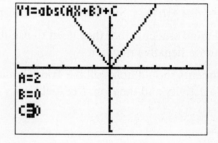

7. Use what you found in Question 6 to complete this conjecture.

   When A = 2, for every increase by 1 in B,
   the vertex moves ? unit(s).

   Set A = 2, B = 0, and C = −2. Test your
   conjecture. Revise your conjecture as needed.

8. Set A = 4, B = 0, and C = 1. Vary the B values and complete the
   conjecture.

   When A = 4, for every increase by 1 in B, the vertex moves ? unit(s).

9. Generalize your findings from the questions above.

   In terms of m, b, and c, the coordinates of the vertex of the graph of
   the absolute value function $y = |mx + b| + c$ are ? .

10. Test your conjecture with the following A, B, and C values. Revise
    your conjecture as needed.

    A = 2, B = 2, C = 4   A = 2, B = 6, C = −2   A = 2, B = −6, C = 2

    A = 4, B = 8, C = −2   A = 4, B = −10, C = −3   A = 4, B = −16, C = 2

Absolute Value Translations I

Activity Objective

Students use the Transformation Graphing App to explore how changing parameter values affects the graph of an absolute value function.

Correlation to Text

- Lesson 2-5: Absolute Value Functions and Graphs

Time

- 30–40 minutes

Materials/Software

- Transformation Graphing App
- Program: A2L25
- Activity worksheet

Skills Needed

- change parameter values

Classroom Management

- This activity can be used as a teacher demonstration.

Notes

- A2L25 uses the form $Y1 = |AX + B| + C$ rather than $y = |mx + b| + c$. Students have to interpret "A" as "m."
- Remind students that they need to use the $(-)$ key, not the subtraction key, to enter a negative number.
- Students should uninstall the Transformation Graphing App when they complete the activity and then run DEFAULT.

Answers

1. $y = |x|; (0, 0)$

2. There is no effect on the vertex. The larger the absolute value of A the steeper the sides of the V.

3. Changing C moves the vertex up or down.   4. Changing B moves the vertex left or right.

5. $(-2, 3); (-4, -2); (1, 3); (4, -1)$

6. Changing C moves the vertex up or down. Changing B moves the vertex left or right.

7. -0.5 8. -0.25

9. $\left(-\frac{b}{m}, c\right)$ 10. Check students' work.

Absolute Value Translations II

For Use With Lesson 2-6

FILES NEEDED: Transformation Graphing App
Program: A2L26

A2L26 graphs the absolute value function $y = |x - b| + c$ (sometimes written $y = |x - h| + k$) as $Y1 = abs(X - B) + C$. In this activity you will study how **B** and **C** are related to vertical and horizontal translations of the graph.

1. Run A2L26 and complete each sentence. The startup graph has B = _?_ and C = _?_. It shows the *parent* absolute value function $y = $ _?_ .

2. Vary the value of C. What is the effect on the graph of $y = |x| + c$ when you increase the value of C? Decrease the value of C?

3. Predict the y-coordinate of the vertex for each function below. Test each prediction by adjusting the value of C on your screen.

$$y = |x| + 3 \qquad y = |x| - 2 \qquad y = |x| + \frac{3}{2}$$

4. Write the absolute value function for each graph shown. Check your answers by drawing each graph with your calculator.

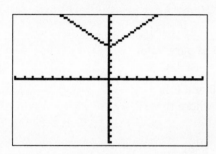 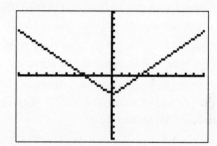

5. Set C = 0. Vary the value of B. What is the effect on the graph of $y = |x - b|$ when you increase the value of B? Decrease the value of B?

6. Write the function equations $y = |x - b|$ for B = 4 and for B = −2. Predict where the vertex will be located in each graph. Test each prediction by adjusting the value of B on your screen.

7. Complete each conjecture.

$y = |x + 4|$ translates the graph of $y = |x|$ by _?_ units to the _?_ .

$y = |x - 5|$ translates the graph of $y = |x|$ by _?_ units _?_ .

8. Generalize your conjectures from Questions 2 and 7.

$y = |x - b| + c$ translates the graph of $y = |x|$ by _?_ and by _?_ .

9. Test your conjecture. Predict the location of the vertex of the graph of each function. Test your predictions by adjusting the screen values of B and C.

$$y = |x - 3| + 2 \qquad y = |x - 4| - 2 \qquad y = |x + 1| - 3 \qquad y = |x + 5| + 4$$

Absolute Value Translations II

Activity Objective

Students use the Transformation Graphing App to investigate horizontal and vertical translations of the absolute value function.

Correlation to Text

- Lesson 2-6: Vertical and Horizontal Translations

Time

- 25–30 minutes

Materials/Software

- Transformation Graphing App
- Program: A2L26
- Activity worksheet

Skills Needed

- change parameter values

Notes

- Discuss the concept of a parent function before this activity. Here students are investigating the translations of the parent function $y = |x|$.

- The Transformation Graphing App uses only A, B, C, and D as parameter names, so $y = |x - h| + k$ appears in the form Y1 = abs(X − B) + C.

- Encourage students to generalize the effects of changes in B and C in this equation form and to watch for similar equation forms where these two constants have the same effects.

- Remind students that they can enter values for B and C directly.

- Students should uninstall the Transformation Graphing App when they complete the activity and then run DEFAULT.

Answers

1. $0; 0; |x|$
2. An increase translates the graph up. A decrease translates the graph down.
3. $3, -2, \frac{3}{2}$
4. $y = |x| + 5; y = |x| - 3$
5. As B increases the graph moves to the right. As B decreases the graph moves to the left.
6. $y = |x - 4|, y = |x + 2|; (4, 0), (-2, 0)$
7. 4, left; 5, to the right
8. b units right for positive values of b and $|b|$ units left for negative values of b; c units up for positive values of c and $|c|$ units down for negative values of c.
9. $(3, 2); (4, -2); (-1, -3); (-5, 4)$

General Inequality Systems

For Use With Lesson 3-3

FILES NEEDED: Inequality Graphing App
Program: A2L33A, A2L33B, A2L33C, A2L33D

Sometimes an inequality in a system of inequalities is nonlinear.
In this activity you practice graphing systems that include such forms.

For each system, describe the graph and boundaries in words. Then draw
the graph. Run the indicated program to check your answers.

1. $y \geq |x - 3| - 2$
$y \leq -3x + 5$

Run **A2L33A** to check. Note that you have to
insert the correct inequality symbols here,
and in each of Questions 2–4.

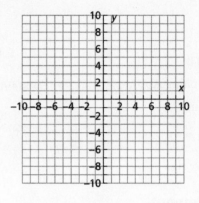

2. $y > 2|x + 1| - 2$
$y \leq 0.5x + 4$

Run **A2L33B** to check.

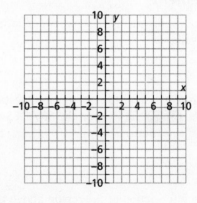

3. $y < -3x + 8$
$y \geq 2x - 3$
$y \leq 5x + 5$

Run **A2L33C** to check.

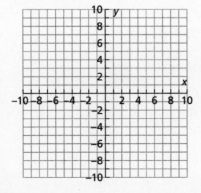

4. $y \leq x^2 - 4$
$y \geq -|x| + 3$
$y < 5$

Run **A2L33D** to check.

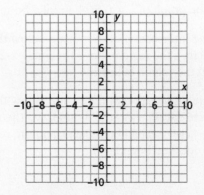

General Inequality Systems

Activity Objective

Students use the Inequality Graphing App to graph systems that include nonlinear inequalities and systems with more than two inequalities.

Correlation to Text

- Lesson 3-3: Systems of Inequalities

Time

- 10–15 minutes

Materials/Software

- Inequality Graphing App
- Activity worksheet
- Programs: A2L33A, A2L33B, A2L33C

Skills Needed

- insert inequality sign

Classroom Management

- Students can work individually or in pairs depending on the number of calculators available.

Notes

- To see the graph of a system even better in Questions 1–4, remind students to press **ALPHA** F2 to open the SHADES menu and then make the correct selection.

Answers

1. The graph is the intersection of the region above the graph of $y = |x - 3| - 2$ [vertex at $(3, -2)$, solid boundary], and the region below the graph of $y = -3x + 5$, solid boundary.

2. The graph is the intersection of the region above the graph of $y = 2|x + 1| - 2$ [vertex at $(-1, -2)$, dashed boundary] and the region below the graph of $y = 0.5x + 4$, solid boundary.

3. The graph is the intersection of the region below the line $y = -3x + 8$ (dashed boundary), the region above the line $y = 2x - 3$ (solid boundary), and the region below the line $y = 5x + 5$ (solid boundary).

4. The graph is the intersection of the region below the parabola $y = x^2 - 4$ [vertex at $(0, -4)$, solid boundary], the region above the graph of $y = -|x| + 3$ (solid boundary), and the region below the graph of $y = 5$ (dashed boundary).

Vertex Principle

> **FILES NEEDED:** Transformation Graphing App
>   Program: A2L34A

In this activity you will use the Transformation Graphing App to support the Vertex Principle of Linear Programming, which states:

If there is a maximum or a minimum value of the linear objective function, it occurs at one or more vertices of the feasible region.

A2L34A graphs the linear equation or function $y = mx + b$ as Y1 = AX + B.

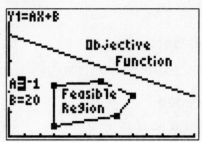

1. Write the equation for the linear function graphed in the startup screen. Write it in slope-intercept form and also in linear objective-function form, $P = ax + by$.

2. For the linear objective function $P = ax + by$, the idea is to find the values of feasible x and y that give the extreme (largest or smallest) value of P. Thus the objective function represents a family of functions determined by all possible values of P. Write the objective function in slope-intercept form.

3. Use your response to Question 2. What is the slope of the graphs of the functions in the family of the objective function? Explain why the slope is constant.

4. What does your response to Question 3 tell you about the graphs of the functions in the family of the objective function?

5. Use your response to Question 2. How are the y-intercepts of the objective function family related to P?

Run A2L34A. The line represents one member of the objective function family whose slope is the constant A; in this case -1.

6. Vary the value of B. Give a plausible argument why the extreme value of the objective function occurs at a vertex of the feasible region.

7. Change the value of the slope, A, to see a member of a different objective function family. Vary B as in Question 6. Is your argument from Question 6 still plausible?

8. Repeat Questions 6 and 7 for **Plot2** and **Plot3**.

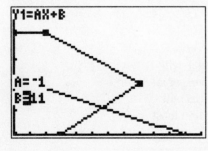
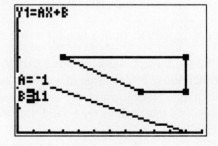

Vertex Principle

Activity Objective

Students use the Transformation Graphing App to help understand the
Vertex Principle of Linear Programming.

Correlation to Text

- Lesson 3-4 : Linear Programming

Time

- 30–35 minutes

Materials/Software

- Transformation Graphing App
- Program: A2L34A
- Activity worksheet

Skills Needed

- change parameter values
- switch plots

Classroom Management

- Students can work individually or in pairs depending on the number
  of calculators available.

Notes

- When you switch to **Plot2** or **Plot3**, the parameter values do not change so
  the initial screens may be different from what you see below Question 8.

- You may want to review with students how to deselect and select a plot
  in either the **Y =** or **STAT PLOT** screens.

Answers

1. $y = -x + 20; 20 = x + y$

2. $y = -\frac{a}{b}x + \frac{P}{b}$

3. $-\frac{a}{b}$; a and b are constants, so $-\frac{a}{b}$ is constant.

4. The graphs have the same slope so they are parallel.

5. The y-intercepts, $\frac{P}{b}$, vary according to all possible values of P.

6. As you vary the y-intercept, the lines in the family $y = -\frac{a}{b}x + \frac{P}{b}$ will
   first, or last, touch the feasible region at a corner, or vertex. Thus, of all
   the lines containing a feasible point, the ones containing vertices will
   give the greatest and least values for $\frac{P}{b}$, and thus the greatest and least
   (feasible) values for P.

7. Yes.

8. Yes for both plots.

Linear Programming

FILES NEEDED: Inequality Graphing App, Transformation Graphing App
Programs: **A2L34B, A2L34C**

In this activity you use the Inequality Graphing App to simplify the solving of linear programming problems.

Run the Inequality Graphing App. Run **A2L34B** and set up the Y= screen as shown below left. Use the SHADES menu (press **ALPHA** F2) to display a "clean" feasibility region, below right, and help you maximize the objective function *Profit* = $0.75x + y$.

   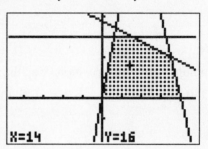

1. Use **Pol-Trace** to find coordinates of the five corner points. Use the cursor to find coordinates of three other feasible points. Record the coordinates in the table and complete the table.

Coordinates of point				(14, 16)			
Value of objective function: *Profit* = $0.75x + y$				$26.50			

2. Which point gives the greatest profit? The least profit? How much in each case?

3. Run the Transformation Graphing App and run **A2L34C**. The startup screen plots the feasibility corner points and a graph of the objective function $P = -0.75x + B$. Translate the graph vertically so it touches some part of the feasibility region but its y-intercept is as large as possible. What value of B gives the greatest y-intercept? At what feasibility point?

4. How do your answers to Questions 2 and 3 compare?

5. Which feasibility point gives maximum profit and what is the maximum profit for a new objective function $P = 2x + y$ or $y = -2x + P$? For a third objective function $P = 10x + y$? (*Hint:* Change the value of A. Then move the graph.)

6. You have used two methods to find the maximum profit. Using the table, you evaluated the objective function at each feasible corner point. Describe the other method.

7. Use the Inequality Graphing App to solve the following linear programming problem. Constraints: $y - x \le 20, 3y + x \le 100, 2y - x \ge 0, y + 0.5x \ge 20$; Objective function to maximize and minimize: $P = y - 2x$.

Linear Programming

Activity Objective

Students use the Inequality Graphing and Transformation Graphing Apps to solve linear programming problems.

Correlation to Text

- Lesson 3-4 : Linear Programming

Time

- 40–45 minutes

Materials/Software

- Inequality Graphing App, Transformation Graphing App
- Programs: A2L34B, A2L34C   • Activity worksheet

Skills Needed

- graph an inequality   • shade an intersection   • change parameter values

Classroom Management

- Students can work individually or in pairs depending on the number of calculators available.

Notes

- Press GRAPH to restore **Shades** and **Pol-Trace** at the bottom of a graph screen.
- PoI in **Pol-Trace** stands for "points of interest."

Answers

1. Non-vertex coordinates may vary. Samples are given.

coordinates	(0, 0)	(40, 0)	(35, 20)	(15, 30)	(6, 30)	(14, 16)	(10, 20)	(20, 10)	(30, 18)
P value	$0	$30	$46.25	$41.25	$34.50	$26.50	$27.50	$25	$40.50

2. $(35, 20)$ for $P = \$46.25$; $(0, 0)$ for $P = \$0$

3. 46.25; $(35, 20)$

4. The greatest profit data in Question 2 match the answers to Question 3.

5. $(35, 20)$, 90; $(40, 0)$, 400

6. Answers may vary. Sample: You graph members of the family $y = ax + P$ and find the line that contains a feasibility point and has the greatest y-intercept.

7. Maximum: $P = 20$ at $(0, 20)$; Minimum: $P = -60$ at $(40, 20)$.

Quadratic Translations I

For Use With Lesson 5-2

FILES NEEDED: Transformation Graphing App

Program: A2L52

A2L52 graphs the quadratic function $y = ax^2 + bx + c$ as
$Y1 = AX^2 + BX + C$. In this activity you will study the relationship
between the vertex of the graph and the values of a, b, and c.

1. Run A2L52. The startup graph has
   $A = 1$, $B = 0$, and $C = 0$. Write the
   equation for this *parent* quadratic function.
   Find its vertex coordinates.

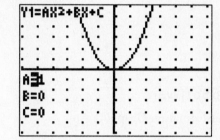

2. Do each of the following. Then describe the
   effects on the vertex and the y-intercept.

   a. Vary the value of A.

   b. Set $A = 1$ and vary the value of C.

   c. Set $C = 2$ and vary the value of B.

   d. Set $A = 2$ and $B = 0$. Then vary the value of C.

   e. Set $C = -2$ and vary the value of B.

   f. Set $A = -4$ and vary the value of B.

3. Generalize. Describe the effect on the graph of $y = ax^2 + bx + c$:

   a. when a changes from $a > 0$ to $a < 0$.

   b. when c changes in increments of 1 or -1.

   c. when $a = 1$ and b changes in increments of 1 or -1.

   d. when $a = 2$ and b changes in increments of 1 or -1.

4. The x-coordinate of the vertex is $-\frac{b}{2a}$. Set $C = 0$. Then choose three
   pairs of values for A and B and check the accuracy of this statement.

5. For each quadratic function below, state whether the parabola opens
   up or down. Also, find the vertex and y-intercept. Enter values for A,
   B, and C directly to check your work.

   a. $y = 2x^2 + 4x - 2$ b. $y = -3x^2 + 6x - 4$ c. $y = 2x^2 - 5x + 1$

Extension

6. What must be true for a, b, and/or c for a quadratic function to have
   a maximum value?

7. How could you find the maximum value? Use your method on 5b.

Quadratic Translations I

Activity Objective

Students use the Transformation Graphing App to explore how changing parameter values in the standard form, $y = ax^2 + bx + c$, of the quadratic function affects the graph of the function.

Correlation to Text

- Lesson 5-2: Properties of Parabolas

Time

- 15–20 minutes

Materials/Software

- Transformation Graphing App
- Program: **A2L52**
- Activity worksheet

Skills Needed

- change parameter values

Notes

- Students should uninstall the Transformation Graphing App when they complete the activity and then run **DEFAULT**.

Answers

1. $y = x^2; (0, 0)$

2. **a.** no effect
    b, d. Vertex and y-intercept are the same and move vertically by an amount equal to the change in C.
    c, e. Vertex traces the path of a parabola opening downward; no effect on y-intercept.
    f. Vertex traces the path of a parabola opening upward; no effect on y-intercept.

3. **a.** The parabola opens in the opposite direction.
    b. Graph moves vertically by an amount equal to the change in C.
    c. Each point of the graph traces the path of a parabola opening downward. Graph moves horizontally by a half unit for each unit change in B.
    d. Like part c, but now graph moves horizontally by a quarter unit for each unit change in B.

4. Check students' work.

5. **a.** up; $(-1, -4)$; -2 **b.** down; $(1, -1)$; -4 **c.** up; $\left(\frac{5}{4}, -2\frac{1}{8}\right)$; 1

6. a must be negative.

7. Let $x = -\frac{b}{2a}$. Substitute for x and solve for y.

Quadratic Translations II

For Use With Lesson 5-3

FILES NEEDED: Transformation Graphing App
Program: A2L53A

In "Quadratic Translations I" you studied translations of the quadratic function in standard form, $y = ax^2 + bx + c$. In this activity, you again study translations of the quadratic function. The translations will build from the parent function, $y = x^2$, to the *vertex form*, $y = a(x - h)^2 + k$.

A2L53A graphs the vertex form as $Y1 = A(X - B)^2 + C$. In the startup window, $A = 1$, $B = 0$, and $C = 0$, and the graph is the parent, $y = x^2$.

1.   Run A2L53A. Vary the value of A. What is the effect on the graph of $Y1 = AX^2$ for increasing values of A? For decreasing values of A? What is the effect on the vertex for changing values of A?

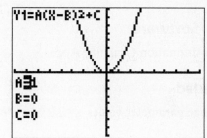

2.   What is the effect on the graph when you change values for A from $A > 0$ to $A < 0$?

3.   Set $A = 1$. Vary the value of B. What is the effect on the graph of $Y1 = (X - B)^2$ for increasing values of B? For decreasing values of B? What is the effect on the vertex for changing values of B?

4.   Predict the vertex x-coordinate for $B = 3$. For $B = -1$. Test your predictions.

5.   With $B \neq 0$, vary the value of A. Compare the effects on the graph of $Y1 = A(X - B)^2$ with the effects on the graph of $Y1 = AX^2$ in Questions 1 and 2.

6.   Vary the value of C. What is the effect on the graph of $Y1 = A(X - B)^2 + C$ for increasing values of C? For decreasing values of C? What is the effect on the vertex for changing values of C?

7.   Copy and complete the following paragraphs to summarize what the vertex form of a quadratic function tells you about the graph.

For $a > 0$ in $y = a(x - h)^2 + k$, the parabola opens __?__. The parabola opens down for __?__. A positive value of h shifts the graph of the parent function to the __?__. A value $h < 0$ shifts the graph to the __?__. The value of h suggests a __?__ (horizontal, vertical) translation of the parent function by __?__ units. The value of k suggests a __?__ translation of the parent function by __?__ units.

The coordinates of the vertex of the graph of $y = a(x - h)^2 + k$ are (__?__, __?__).

Extension

8.   Write each function in vertex form and describe the graph.

   a. $y - 5 = -2(x - 3)^2$ **b.** $y = x^2 - 6x + 9$ **c.** $y = 2x^2 + 6x + 1$

Quadratic Translations II

Activity Objective

Students use the Transformation Graphing App to explore how changing parameter values in the vertex form, $y = a(x - h)^2 + k$, of the quadratic function affects the graph of the function.

Correlation to Text

- Lesson 5-3: Translating Parabolas

Time

- 15–20 minutes

Materials/Software

- Transformation Graphing App
- Program: **A2L53A**
- Activity worksheet

Skills Needed

- change parameter values

Notes

- Remind students of the similarities between these transformations and the ones they studied earlier in the course.
- Compare (X + 3) with (X − B) and show that B must be −3.
- Students should uninstall the Transformation Graphing App when they complete the activity and then run **DEFAULT**.

Answers

1. Increasing A narrows the graph vertically. Decreasing A, A > 0, widens the graph. Changing values of A has no effect on the vertex.

2. If A > 0, the graph opens up. If A < 0, the graph opens down.

3. Increasing B moves the graph (and vertex) to the right. Decreasing B moves the graph (and vertex) to the left. The coordinates of the vertex are (B, 0).

4. 3; −1   5.   The effects are the same.

6. Increasing C moves the graph (and vertex) up. Decreasing C moves the graph (and vertex) down.

7. up; A < 0; right; left; horizontal; $|h|$; vertical; $|k|$; h; k

8. a. $y = -2(x - 3)^2 + 5$, parabola, vertex $(3, 5)$, opens down
   b. $y = (x - 3)^2$, parabola, vertex $(3, 0)$, opens up
   c. $y = 2(x + 1.5)^2 - 3.5$, parabola, vertex $(-1.5, -3.5)$, opens up.

Name _____ Class _____ Date _____

Dodge 'Em

For Use With Lesson 5-3

FILES NEEDED: Transformation Graphing App
Program: A2L53B

You are the captain of a space freighter. You have to make deliveries to space stations A, B, and C.

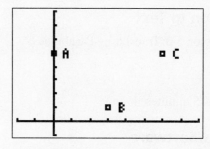

Unfortunately, space is not clear. There are asteroids (+) in the plane of your path. You must not collide with an asteroid.

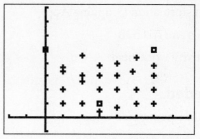

There is a safe parabolic path that runs through the asteroid field and connects the space stations.

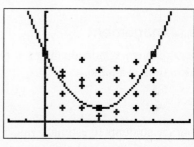

You must find it.

A2L53B graphs the vertex form $y = a(x - h)^2 + k$ of a quadratic function as Y1 = A(X − B)^2 + C with A = 1, B = 0, and C = 0.

Run A2L53B and find values of A, B, and C that will miss the asteroids. Record the vertex form of the successful quadratic function in your Captain's Log.

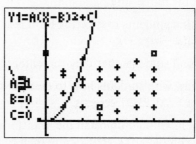

Extension

Switch from **Plot1** to **Plot2** (keeping **Plot3** active) and press GRAPH for a more challenging space flight. Find a function to guide your spacecraft safely to the three space stations.

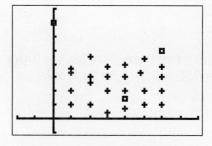

Dodge 'Em

Activity Objective

Students use the Transformation Graphing App to practice translating the graph of a parabola by changing the parameter values in $Y1 = A(X - B)^2 + C$.

Correlation to Text

- Lesson 5-3: Translating Parabolas

Time

- 10–15 minutes

Materials/Software

- Transformation Graphing App
- Program: A2L53B
- Activity worksheet

Skills Needed

- change parameter values
- select and deselect a plot

Classroom Management

- Students can work individually or in pairs depending on the number of calculators available.

Notes

- Encourage students to estimate values for A, B, and C before they start to "move" the parabola.
- Remind students that vertex form is shown in the text as $y = a(x - h)^2 + k$
- Remind students that they can enter values for A and B directly.
- Review with students how to deselect and select a plot in either the Y= or STAT PLOT screens.
- Students should uninstall the Transformation Graphing App when they complete the activity and then run DEFAULT.

Answers

Answers may vary. Samples: $y = 0.45(x - 3) + 1$ for **Plot1**; $y = 0.5(x - 3.3) + 1.4$ for **Plot2**.

Quadratic Function Match II

For Use With Lesson 5-3

FILES NEEDED: Transformation Graphing App
                Program: **A2L53C**

A2L53C graphs the vertex form of the quadratic function, $y = a(x - h)^2 + k$, as **Y1 = A(X − B)² + C** with **A = 1, B = 0**, and **C = 0**.

In this activity you see three plots, one at a time. You are to change the values of **A**, **B**, and **C** to find a perfect match for the given plot.

1. Run **A2L53C**. Find a quadratic function whose graph matches the plot.

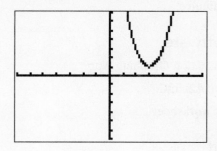

2. Switch from **Plot1** to **Plot2**. Press **GRAPH** to see **A2L53C** for the second plot. Find a matching quadratic function.

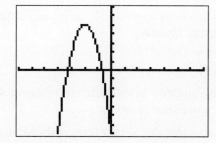

3. Switch from **Plot2** to **Plot3**. Press **GRAPH** to see **A2L53C** for the third plot. Find a matching quadratic function.

4. Write the three functions found in Questions 1–3 in standard form. Draw their graphs in the respective Plots of **A2L53C**. How can you tell whether your standard form is correct?

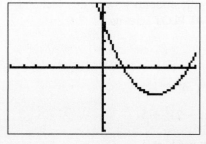

Quadratic Function Match II

Activity Objective

Students use the Transformation Graphing App to practice translating the graph of a parabola by changing the parameter values in $Y1 = A(X - B)^2 + C$.

Correlation to Text

- Lesson 5-3: Translating Parabolas

Time

- 10–15 minutes

Materials/Software

- Transformation Graphing App
- Program: A2L53C
- Activity worksheet

Skills Needed

- change parameter values
- select and deselect a plot

Classroom Management

- Students can work individually or in pairs depending on the number of calculators available.

Notes

- Encourage students to estimate the values of A, B, and C before they start to "move" the parabola.
- Remind students that vertex form is shown in the text as
  $y = a(x - h)^2 + k$.
- Remind students that they can enter values for A and B directly.
- Review with students how to deselect and select a plot in either the Y= or STAT PLOT screens.

Answers

1. $y = 2(x - 3)^2 + 1$

2. $y = -3(x + 2)^2 + 5$

3. $y = 0.5(x - 4)^2 - 3$

4. $y = 2x^2 - 12x + 19$; $y = -3x^2 - 12x - 7$; $y = 0.5x^2 - 4x + 5$; It is correct if the graphs are identical.

Follow the Bouncing Ball I

> **FILES NEEDED:** Transformation Graphing App
>   Program A2L53D

For this activity, a motion detector collected data about a bouncing ball. The graph at the right shows a plot of the data. You are to find models for some of the data.

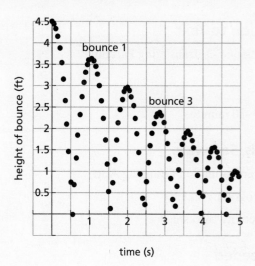

1. Use the graph. On which bounce did the ball go the highest? How do you know?

2. About how high did the ball go on its first bounce?

3. Approximately how long was the ball in the air on its first bounce? On its fifth bounce?

4. Run A2L53D. It graphs the vertex form of the quadratic function, $y = a(x - h)^2 + k$, as $Y1 = A(X - B)^2 + C$. Change the values of A, B, and C to find a model for the first bounce. Write the function equation for your model.

5. Find a function equation that models the third bounce.

6. For the first and third bounces, how are the two values of A related?

7. How do the two values of B compare? The two values of C?

8. What do you suppose are the "real world" meanings of B and C?

Extension

9. Do you think the motion detector found the actual vertex point on each bounce? Explain.

10. The pictures below show the data collected during the second bounce. Do these plots show the actual vertex? Explain.

11. If the motion detector does not find the actual vertex, how could you find it?

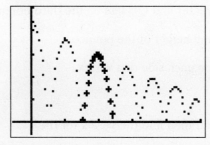

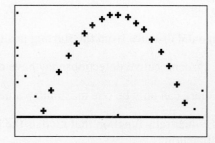

Algebra 2 Lesson 5-3 (fourth activity)

Follow the Bouncing Ball I

Activity Objective

Students use the Transformation Graphing App to model the bounce of a ball based on bounce data gathered by a motion detector.

Correlation to Text

- Lesson 5-3: Translating Parabolas

Time

- 20–30 minutes

Materials/Software

- Transformation Graphing App
- Program: A2L53D
- Activity worksheet

Skills Needed

- change parameter values

Classroom Management

- Students can work individually or in pairs depending on the number of calculators available.

Notes

- Students should realize while answering Question 6 that the A values should be the same if they aren't already.

Answers

1. bounce 1; it has the highest peak

2. 3.7 ft

3. 1 s; 0.5 s

4–6. Answers may vary. Samples are given.

4. $y = -14.9(x - 1.05)^2 + 3.7$

5. $y = -14.9(x - 2.84)^2 + 2.5$

6. They are the same.

7. B is greater and C is less on the third bounce.

8. B is the horizontal distance from the starting position. C is the height of the bounce.

9. Not necessarily; consecutive detections may have occurred on each side of a vertex.

10. No, because there can only be one maximum value.

11. You can find a quadratic function that models the bounce and then find the vertex for the graph of the function.

Graphs, Zeros, and Factors

For Use With Lesson 6-2

FILES NEEDED: Transformation Graphing App
Program: A2L62A

In A2L62A, the polynomial function $y = (x - a)(x - b)(x - c)$ is in *factored form* and is graphed as Y1 = (X − A)(X − B)(X − C).

In this activity you will explore relationships among

- the *x*-intercepts or *zeros* of a polynomial function,
- the solutions of the related polynomial equation, and
- the factors of the related polynomial expression.

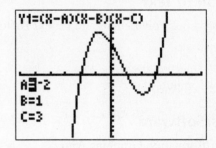

1. Run **A2L62A**. What are the values of A, B, and C in the startup window? What is the function whose graph is shown?

2. The polynomial function $y = (x - a)(x - b)(x - c)$ has $(x - a)(x - b)(x - c) = 0$ as its *related polynomial equation*. What is the related polynomial equation for the function you found in Question 1?

3. Explain both algebraically and graphically why $a, b,$ and c are the zeros of the polynomial function $y = (x - a)(x - b)(x - c)$. What are the zeros of the polynomial function you found in Question 1?

4. $y = ax^3 + bx^2 + cx + d$ is the *standard form* of the function $y = (x - a)(x - b)(x - c)$. (*Note: a, b,* and *c* in the two forms do not represent the same values.) Write the standard form of the polynomial function you found in Question 1. Write its corresponding polynomial equation. What are the solutions of this equation? Explain how you know.

5. Change the value of A as indicated. Describe the effect on the graph and on the solutions of each related polynomial equation.

  a. Set A = −1   **b.** Set A = 0   **c.** Set A = 1

6. Draw a sketch to predict what the graph of each function will look like. Use **A2L62A** to test your predictions.

  a. $y = (x - 1)(x - 2)(x - 3)$ **b.** $y = (x - 1)^2(x - 3)$ **c.** $y = (x - 1)^3$

7. For each polynomial, graph the function. Use the graph to factor the polynomial. Solve the related polynomial equation.

  a. $x^3 - 2x^2 - 16x + 32$ **b.** $x^3 + 8x^2 - 4x - 32$ **c.** $x^4 - 3x^3 - 15x^2 + 19x + 30$
  d. $x^4 - 9x^2 + 4x + 12$ **e.** $-x^3 - 2x^2 + 5x + 6$ **f.** $x^4 - 5x^3 + 6x^2 + 4x - 8$

Extension

8. How many solutions are possible for a polynomial equation that uses a polynomial of degree 2? Degree 3? Degree 4? Degree *n*?

Graphs, Zeros, and Factors

Activity Objective

Students use the Transformation Graphing App to explore the relationships among the *x*-intercepts of a polynomial function, the zeros of the function, the solutions of the related polynomial equation, and the factors of the related polynomial expression.

Correlation to Text

- Lesson 6-2: Polynomials and Linear Factors

Time

- 40–45 minutes

Materials/Software

- Transformation Graphing App
- Program: **A2L62A**
- Activity worksheet

Skills Needed

- change parameter values

Notes

- Remind students that they can enter A and B values directly.
- Students should uninstall the Transformation Graphing App when they complete the activity and then run **DEFAULT**.

Answers

1. $-2, 1, 3; y = (x + 2)(x - 1)(x - 3)$ 2. $(x + 2)(x - 1)(x - 3) = 0$

3. $a, b,$ and c are zeros because $y = 0$ when $x = a, x = b,$ or $x = c.$
   Graphically, $a, b,$ and c are the x-intercepts (where $y = 0$). $-2, 1, 3$

4. $y = x^3 - 2x^2 - 5x + 6; x^3 - 2x^2 - 5x + 6 = 0;$ This equation is equivalent to the Question 2 equation, so their solutions are the same, $-2, 1, 3.$

5. **a.** A zero and a solution change from -2 to $-1.$
   b. A zero and a solution change to 0.
   c. The graph touches but does not cross the x-axis at $x = 1.$
   There are only two solutions, 1 and 3.

6. Check students' graphs. **a.** zeros at $1, 2, 3$ **b.** See Question 5, part c.
   c. The graph intersects the x-axis once—at $(1, 0).$

7. **a.** $-4, 2, 4$ **b.** $-8, -2, 0$ **c.** $-3, -1, 2, 5$
   d. $-3, -1, 2$ **e.** $-3, -1, 2$ **f.** $-1, 2$

8. $2; 3; 4; n$

Polynomial Function Match

For Use With Lesson 6-2

FILES NEEDED: Transformation Graphing App
                  Program: **A2L62B**

A2L62B graphs the factored form, $y = (x - a)(x - b)(x - c)$, of the polynomial function as Y1 = (X − A)(X − B)(X − C).

In this activity you see three plots, one at a time. You are to change the values of A, B, and C to find a perfect match for the given plot.

1.   Run **A2L62B**. Find a polynomial function whose graph matches the plot.

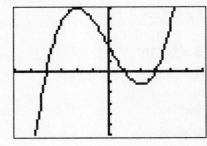

2.   Switch from **Plot1** to **Plot2**. Press **GRAPH** to see **A2L62B** for the second plot. Find a matching polynomial function.

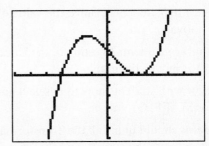

3.   Switch from **Plot2** to **Plot3**. Press **GRAPH** to see **A2L62B** for the third plot. Find a matching polynomial function.

4.   Explain how you could have answered Questions 1–3 without manipulating values for A, B, and C.

5.   Write the three functions found in Questions 1–3 in standard form. Draw their graphs in the respective Plots of **A2L62B**. How can you tell whether your standard form is correct?

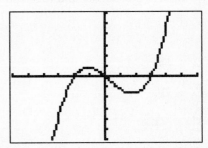

Extension

6.   For all three graphs above, explain the behavior of the parts of the graphs that are not shown (sometimes called *end behavior*). What could you do to one of the given functions to make this type of behavior occur in Quadrants II and IV instead of I and III?

Polynomial Function Match

Activity Objective

Students use the Transformation Graphing App to explore how changing parameter values in the factored form $y = (x - a)(x - b)(x - c)$ of the polynomial function affects the graph of the function.

Correlation to Text

- Lesson 6-2: Polynomials and Linear Factors

Time

- 25–30 minutes

Materials/Software

- Transformation Graphing App
- Program: **A2L62B**
- Activity worksheet

Skills Needed

- change parameter values
- deselect and select a plot

Notes

- Suggest that students change the value of **A** to find which graph is the "movable" one.

- Encourage students to estimate the values of **A**, **B**, and **C** before they start to "move" the graph.

- Review with students how to deselect and select a plot in either the **Y=** or **STAT PLOT** screens.

- Students should uninstall the Transformation Graphing App when they complete the activity and then run **DEFAULT**.

Answers

1. $y = (x + 4)(x - 1)(x - 3)$

2. $y = (x + 3)(x - 2)^2$

3. $y = x(x + 2)(x - 3)$

4. The zeros of the function are the values a, b, and c.

5. $y = x^3 - 13x + 12$; $y = x^3 - x^2 - 8x + 12$; $y = x^3 - x^2 - 6x$;
   The graphs will match the graphs given in the Plots.

6. As $|x|$ becomes arbitrarily large, $|y|$ becomes arbitrarily large. You can reflect the graph across the x-axis by introducing a factor of -1.

Radical Translations I

> **FILES NEEDED:** Transformation Graphing App
> Program: **A2L78A**

In the "Quadratic Translations II" Activity for Lesson 5-3, you studied translations of the quadratic function, building from the parent function $y = x^2$ to a general form that you can write as $y = a(x - b)^2 + c$.

In this activity you will study translations of the radical function, building from the parent function $y = \sqrt{x}$ to the general form $y = a\sqrt{x - b} + c$. You should notice that the two general forms are quite similar. It turns out that the effects of $a, b,$ and c on the graphs of the functions are quite similar as well.

A2L78A graphs the square root function $y = a\sqrt{x - b} + c$ as $Y1 = A\sqrt{(X - B)} + C$.

1. Run **A2L78A**. Write the function equation for the graph shown in the startup window. What special name does this function have? Describe its domain and range.

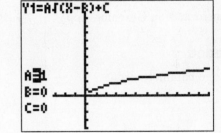

2. Recall the effects of change in c on the graph of $y = a(x - b)^2 + c$. Predict how change in c will affect the graph of $y = a\sqrt{x - b} + c$.

3. Test your prediction. Change the value of **C** in increments of 1. What happens to the graph? Use increments of -1. What happens to the graph?

4. Recall the effect of change in b on the graph of $y = a(x - b)^2 + c$. Predict how change in b will affect the graph of $y = a\sqrt{x - b} + c$.

5. Test your prediction. Set **C** = 0. Change the value of **B** in increments of 1. What happens? In increments of -1. What happens?

6. For each given function, what are the values of c and b? Describe the translation of the parent graph. Give the domain and range.

   a. $y = \sqrt{x} + 2$ **b.** $y = \sqrt{x} - 3$ **c.** $y = \sqrt{x - 3}$ **d.** $y = \sqrt{x + 2}$

7. For the function $y = \sqrt{x - 3} + 4$, describe two translations of the parent graph that result in the graph of this function. Give the domain and range. Use **A2L78A** to check your work.

8. Predict how changes in a will affect the graph of $y = a\sqrt{x - b} + c$. Use **A2L78A** to change **A** and check your predictions.

9. Shift the graph of $y = \sqrt{x}$ by 2 units down and 3 units left. What is the function equation for the new graph. Check using **A2L78A**.

10. Describe how the graph of each relates to the graph of $y = \sqrt{x}$.

    a. $y = 2\sqrt{x - 5} + 4$ **b.** $y = \frac{1}{2}\sqrt{x + 1} - 4$ **c.** $y = -4\sqrt{x + 3} + 6$

Radical Translations I

Activity Objective

Students use the Transformation Graphing App to explore how changing parameter values in the square root function $y = a\sqrt{x - b} + c$ affects the graph of the function.

Correlation to Text

- Lesson 7-8: Graphing Radical Functions

Time

- 40–45 minutes

Materials/Software

- Transformation Graphing App
- Program: A2L78A
- Activity worksheet

Skills Needed

- change parameter values

Answers

1. $y = \sqrt{x}$; square root function; domain: $x \geq 0$, range: $y \geq 0$.

2. Moves the graph vertically by an amount equal to the change in c.

3. Moves up in steps of 1; moves down in steps of 1.

4. Moves the graph horizontally by an amount equal to the change in b.

5. Moves right in steps of 1; moves left in steps of 1.

6. **a.** 2, 0; moves up 2 units; domain: $x \geq 0$, range: $y \geq 2$.

    b. $-3, 0$; moves down 3 units; domain: $x \geq 0$, range: $y \geq -3$.

    c. 0, 3; moves right 3 units; domain: $x \geq 3$, range: $y \geq 0$.

    d. 0, -2; moves left 2 units; domain: $x \geq -2$, range: $y \geq 0$.

7. Moves up 4 units and right 3 units; domain: $x \geq 3$, range: $y \geq 4$.

8. Increase in a will stretch the graph vertically. Decrease in a ($a > 0$) will shrink the graph vertically. A sign change in a will reflect the graph across the line $y = c$.

9. $y = \sqrt{x + 3} - 2$

10. For each of a–c, begin with the graph of $y = \sqrt{x}$.
    a. Shift right 5, stretch vertically by factor of 2, shift up 4.
    b. Shift left 1, shrink vertically by factor of $\frac{1}{2}$, shift down 4.
    c. Shift left 3, stretch vertically by factor of 4, reflect across x-axis, shift up 6.

Radical Translations II

For Use With Lesson 7-8

> **FILES NEEDED:** Transformation Graphing App
>   Program: A2L78B

In "Radical Translations I" you studied translations of the square root function, building from the parent function $y = \sqrt{x}$ to the general form $y = a\sqrt{x - b} + c$. You can take the general form further—to the nth-root function, $y = a\sqrt[n]{x - b} + c$.

A2L78B graphs the nth-root function using Y1, Y2, and Y3, as shown at the right.

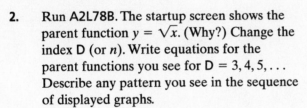

1. For each of Y1, Y2, and Y3, complete the following using $a, b, c,$ and n.

    $y_1 = \underline{\ ?\ }$ $y_2 = \underline{\ ?\ }$ $y_3 = \underline{\ ?\ }$

2. Run A2L78B. The startup screen shows the parent function $y = \sqrt{x}$. (Why?) Change the index D (or n). Write equations for the parent functions you see for $D = 3, 4, 5, \ldots$ Describe any pattern you see in the sequence of displayed graphs.

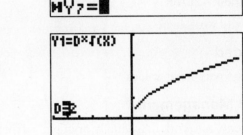

3. Graphs of quadratic and absolute value functions have a *vertex* that you can use as a central point for describing translations. What point can you use as the *central translation point* for a parent radical function whose index is an odd number? An even number?

4. What are the domain and range of the parent nth-root function $y = \sqrt[n]{x}$ when n is even? When n is odd?

5. As you might suspect, the effects of $a, b,$ and c on the graphs of $y = a\sqrt{x - b} + c$ and $y = a\sqrt[n]{x - b} + c$ are the same. Use what you know about the square root function to predict how the graph of the parent cube root function translates to the graph of each function given below.

    a. $y = \sqrt[3]{x - 3} + 1$ **b.** $y = \sqrt[3]{x + 1} - 2$ **c.** $y = -\sqrt[3]{x} + 2$

    Use A2L78B to test your predictions. In the Y= window (see top of page), select Y2 by highlighting its "=" sign. Then press GRAPH.

6. For each function below, list the domain and range, and sketch a graph. Use Y2 and Y3 in A2L78B to check your sketches.

    a. $y = \sqrt[3]{x + 5} - 2$ **b.** $y = \sqrt[4]{x} + 3$

    c. $y = -\sqrt[3]{x + 2} + 3$ **d.** $y = 2\sqrt[4]{x} + 3$

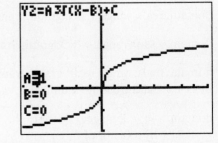

Radical Translations II

Activity Objective

Students use the Transformation Graphing App to study the effect of n on the graphs of the parent radical function $y = \sqrt[n]{x}$, and to explore how changing other parameter values in $y = a\sqrt[n]{x - b} + c$ affects the graph of the function.

Correlation to Text

- Lesson 7-8: Graphing Radical Functions

Time

- 40–45 minutes

Materials/Software

- Transformation Graphing App
- Program: A2L78B
- Activity worksheet

Skills Needed

- change parameter values

Classroom Management

- Students can work individually or in pairs depending on the number of calculators available.

Answers

1. $y_1 = \sqrt[n]{x}; y_2 = a\sqrt[3]{x - b} + c; y_3 = a\sqrt[4]{x - b} + c$

2. $y = \sqrt[3]{x}, y = \sqrt[4]{x}, y = \sqrt[5]{x}, \ldots$; Answers may vary. Sample: When n is odd, the graphs of $y = \sqrt[n]{x}$ show similar behavior in Quadrants I and III. When n is even, the graphs show similar behavior in Quadrant I and don't appear anywhere else.

3. $(0, 0); (0, 0)$

4. nonnegative real numbers; real numbers

5. a. Translates right 3 and up 1.

   b. Translates left 1 and down 2.

   c. Reflects across the x-axis and translates up 2.

6. a. domain: reals; range: reals; graph: translate $y = \sqrt[3]{x}$ by 5 units left and 2 units down.

   b. domain: $x \geq 0$; range: $y \geq 3$; graph: translate $y = \sqrt[4]{x}$ by 3 units up.

   c. domain: reals; range: reals; graph: translate $y = \sqrt[3]{x}$ by 2 units left, reflect across the x-axis, and translate 3 units up.

   d. domain: $x \geq -3$; range: $y \geq 0$; graph: translate $y = \sqrt[4]{x}$ by 3 units left and stretch vertically by a factor of 2.

Name _____ Class _____ Date _____

Choose a Model II

For Use With Lesson 8-1

> **FILES NEEDED:** Transformation Graphing App
> Program: A2L81A

In A2L81A, you will view three plots, one at a time. You are to select the appropriate family of functions and then use the Transformation Graphing App to find a family member that models the displayed data.

Function Families

Linear	Quadratic	Exponential
$y = mx + b$	$y = a(x - b)^2 + c$	$y = ab^x$
Y1 = AX + B	Y2 = A(X − B)^2 + C	Y3 = AB^X

```
Plot1  Plot2  Plot3
\Y1=AX+B
\Y2=A(X-B)²+C
\Y3=AB^X
\Y4=■
\Y5=
\Y6=
\Y7=
```

The numbers a, b, and c are called *parameters*. For each plot there is a "perfect" model. Choose Y1, Y2, or Y3 and be prepared to take parameter values to two decimal places to find the perfect model.

1. Run A2L81A. In the Y= window, select the function you think will give the best model by highlighting its "=" sign. Then press **GRAPH**. Change the parameter values until you have the graph passing through the plotted points. Write the function for your graph.

2. Switch from Plot1 to Plot2. Press **GRAPH** to see the second plot. Select a function. Change its parameter values to get the perfect model. Write the function for your graph.

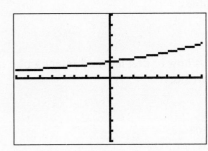

3. Switch from Plot2 to Plot3.

   Press **GRAPH** to see the third plot. Select a function. Change its parameter values to get the perfect model. Write the function for your graph.

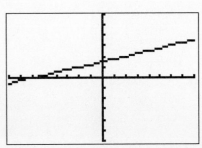

Extension

4. Suppose you had to make a "Choose a Model" challenge for a classmate. How would you construct the given plot?

TI-83/84 Plus Activities

Algebra 2 Lesson 8-1 (first activity)

125

Choose a Model II

Activity Objective

Students make a visual choice of an appropriate model and then use the Transformation Graphing App to confirm their choice.

Correlation to Text

- Lesson 8-1: Exploring Exponential Models

Time

- 20–25 minutes

Materials/Software

- Transformation Graphing App
- Program: A2L81A
- Activity worksheet

Skills Needed

- change parameter values
- select and deselect a plot

Classroom Management

- Students can work individually or in pairs depending on the number of calculators available.

Notes

- Review with students how to deselect and select a plot in either the Y= or STAT PLOT screens.

Answers

1. $y = -2(x + 5)^2 + 3$

2. $y = 1.5(1.1)^x$

3. $y = 0.25x + 1.5$

4. Check students' work.

Follow the Bouncing Ball II

FILES NEEDED: Transformation Graphing App
                Program: **A2L81B**

The graph at the right shows the plot of the motion-detector data gathered for a bouncing ball and used in "Follow the Bouncing Ball I." In that activity you found equations that modeled some of the bounces.

In this activity you will find a relationship between bounce number and height. Based on the graph:

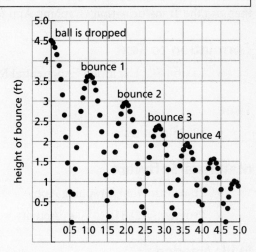

1. From what height was the ball dropped?

2. How high was bounce 1?

3. How long was the ball in the air during bounce 1?

4. Complete the following table. Heights are in feet.

Bounce number	Maximum bounce height	Difference of this height from previous height	Ratio of this height to previous height
0	4.5		
1	3.7	$4.5 - 3.7 = 0.8$	$\frac{3.7}{4.5} \approx 0.82$
2			
3			
4			
5			

5. Study the data in the table. Of the functions you have studied so far—linear, absolute value, quadratic, radical, and exponential—which do you think would make the best model for the relationship between the bounce number and the bounce height? Explain. Then write a function equation that you feel would be a good model for the relationship between bounce number and bounce height.

6. Run A2L81B. Trace on the plot and compare with the first two columns of your table. If close, you do not need to change your table. Choose Y1, Y2, or Y3 (highlight the "=" sign and press ENTER) to match your choice of function in Question 5. Press GRAPH and change the A, B, C values to make the best model you can. Record the function equation for your model.

7. Use your model. When will the bounce height be less than one foot?

8. According to your model, will the ball ever stop bouncing? Explain.

Follow the Bouncing Ball II

Activity Objective

Students make a choice of an appropriate model based on tabular data and then use the Transformation Graphing App to confirm their choice.

Correlation to Text

- Lesson 8-1: Exploring Exponential Models

Time

- 20–25 minutes

Materials/Software

- Transformation Graphing App
- Program: A2L81B
- Activity worksheet

Skills Needed

- change parameter values

Classroom Management

- Students can work individually or in pairs depending on the number of calculators available.

Notes

- Review with students how to deselect and select a plot in either the Y= or STAT PLOT screens.

Answers

1. 4.5 ft

2. about 3.7 ft

3. 1 s

4. Answers may vary. Sample:

2	2.9	0.8	0.78
3	2.4	0.5	0.83
4	1.9	0.5	0.79
5	1.6	0.3	0.84

5. Answers may vary. Sample: Exponential; Only for an expontential relationship would the points lie on a curve with an asymptote; $y = 4.5(0.8)^x$

6. Answers may vary. Sample: $y = 4.5(0.8)^x$.

7. bounce 7

8. No; $y > 0$ for all x.

Asymptotes for Exponentials

For Use With Lesson 8-2

FILES NEEDED: Transformation Graphing App
Programs: A2L82A, A2L82B

A2L82A graphs the exponential function $y = ab^x + c$
as Y1 = AB^X + C.

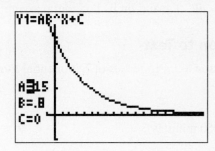

In this activity you will investigate the effects of
changes in a, b, and c on the graph of the exponential
function and its asymptote.

1. Run **A2L82A**. Write the function equation
   for the startup graph. Explain why the
   function is decreasing as x gets large. Which
   line is a horizontal asymptote for the graph?
   Explain.

2. Predict what will happen to the asymptote of the graph when you vary the value of **C**.
   Test your prediction. (*Note:* On the y-axis the scale marks are 5 units apart.)

3. When you vary **C**, you change the y-intercept as well as the asymptote. For $y = ab^x + c$
   in general, what is the equation of the asymptote? What is the y-intercept? Use **A2L82A**
   and the following functions to test your answers.

   a. $y = 8(0.3)^x + 4$ **b.** $y = 10(0.9)^x + 2$ **c.** $y = 10(0.8)^x - 5$ **d.** $y = 15(0.75)^x - 4$

4. Run **A2L82B**. The startup screen shows a scatter
   plot for the "Cooling Coffee" data on page 430 of
   your textbook. Vary **A**, **B**, and **C** to find a function
   model for the data. (Use two decimal places for
   B.) Give the asymptote and the y-intercept. Tell
   what each means in terms of the cooling coffee.

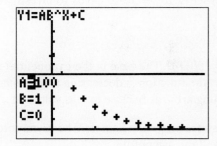

5. If the coffee was 135°F above room temperature
   and room temperature was 72°F, what would be
   the coffee temperature?

6. Switch from **Plot1** to **Plot2**. The plotted data represent the actual
   temperature of the same cooling coffee in a room temperature of
   72°F. Vary **A**, **B**, and **C** to find a function model for the data.
   Compare the model with your model from Question 4. Tell how the
   cooling-coffee data was adjusted for **Plot2**.

7. Suppose the same coffee cup was used on another day when room
   temperature was 70°F and the actual temperature of the coffee was
   only 180°F at time 0. Write an equation that you think would model
   the cooling-coffee temperature. Explain your choices for a, b, and c.

8. Switch from **Plot2** to **Plot3**. Find a function model for the data.
   (*Hint:* Find values for a and c first.)

Asymptotes for Exponentials

Activity Objective

Students use the Transformation Graphing App to study the effects of changes in the values of a, b, and c, on the graph of the exponential function $y = ab^x + c$ and on its horizontal asymptote.

Correlation to Text

- Lesson 8-2: Properties of Exponential Functions

Time

- 40–50 minutes

Materials/Software

- Transformation Graphing App
- Programs: **A2L82A, A2L82B**
- Activity worksheet

Notes

- Review with students how to deselect and select a plot in either the Y= or STAT PLOT screens.
- To help verify answers in Question 3, students can trace along the graphs.
- In Question 8, after finding values for a and c, students may find it instructive to set **Step** = 0.01 to investigate values of b.

Answers

1. $y = 15(0.8)^x$. The base in the exponential function is between 0 and 1, so the function is decreasing as x gets large. $y = 0$; values of y are getting arbitrarily close to 0 as values of x get arbitrarily large.

2. Answers may vary. Sample: The asymptote is $y = c$, so as c changes, so will the asymptote.

3. $y = c; a + c$ **a.** $y = 4; 12$ **b.** $y = 2; 12$ **c.** $y = -5; 5$ **d.** $y = -4; 11$

4. Answers may vary. Sample: $y = 135(0.95)^x$. $y = 0$ (the amount room temperature is above room temperature); 135 (the temperature of the coffee above room temperature at time $x = 0$)

5. 207°F   6. Answers may vary. Sample: $y = 135(0.95)^x + 72$. Each coffee temperature value was increased by 72.

7. $y = 110(0.95)^x + 70$. Let $b = 0.95$ since the cooling substance is still coffee. Let $c = 70$, the room temperature, which is what y must approach as x gets large. Let $a = 110$, which is how much warmer than room temperature the coffee is at time $x = 0$.

8. Answers may vary. Sample: $y = 140(0.85)^x + 20$.

Asymptotes for Rationals .... For Use With Lesson 9-2

> **FILES NEEDED:** Transformation Graphing App
> Program: **A2L92**

The function $y = \frac{1}{x}$, sometimes known as the inverse function, is the parent for the family of rational functions, $y = \frac{a}{x - b} + c$. The parent function has the two axes as its asymptotes, as shown on page 485 of your textbook.

Because a rational function graph has two branches, it sometimes is difficult to get a good calculator view of the graph. On the other hand, if your calculator is in Connected Mode, the "connect" between the two branches (see right) will suggest the vertical asymptote!

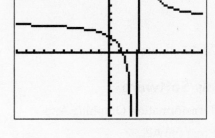

In this activity, you will study the effects of changes in a, b, and c on the graphs of rational functions and particularly on their asymptotes. In fact, if you understand the effects of changes in the parameters on other families of functions, you already know how the changes will affect this family.

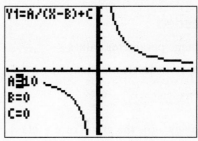

1. Run **A2L92**. Write the function equation for the graph shown on the startup screen. Compare its a value with that of the parent function. Tell how its graph compares to the graph of the parent function.

2. Predict how the graph will change when you change the value of **B**. Test your prediction with three different values for **B**. For each value, write the equations of the function and of both asymptotes.

3. Repeat Question 2 for **C**.

4. What are the equations of the asymptotes when **B** = −3 and **C** = 2?

5. Write equations for both asymptotes of each graph. Use **A2L92** to check.

   a. $y = \frac{10}{x} + 2$ **b.** $y = \frac{10}{x - 2}$ **c.** $y = \frac{10}{x - 2} + 3$ **d.** $y = \frac{10}{x + 2} - 3$

6. Activate **Plot1**, **Plot2**, and **Plot3**, each in turn. For each graph, change parameter values in **Y1 = A/(X − B) + C** to make a matching graph. Write the function equation you find. Don't forget, you can change **A**.

   a. 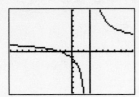   **b.** 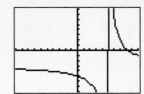   **c.**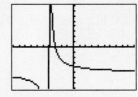

Asymptotes for Rationals

Activity Objective

Students use the Transformation Graphing App to study the connections between the values of b and c and the asymptotes of the rational function $y = \frac{a}{x - b} + c$.

Correlation to Text

- Lesson 9-2: Graphing Inverse Variations

Time

- 20–25 minutes

Materials/Software

- Transformation Graphing App
- Program: A2L92
- Activity worksheet

Skills Needed

- change parameter values
- select or deselect a plot

Notes

- Review how the graph of $y = a(x + b)^2 + c$ changes as $a, b,$ and c change. Have students look for similar patterns for rational function graphs.
- Discuss how to use TRACE to check values for asymptotes.

Answers

1. $y = \frac{10}{x}$; for $y = \frac{10}{x}$, the value of a is 10. In the parent function, the value of a is 1. For both graphs the asymptotes are the x- and y-axes. The branches of $y = \frac{10}{x}$ are farther from the origin than the branches of $y = \frac{1}{x}$

2. The graph will shift horizontally by an amount equal to the change in B.

3. The graph will shift vertically by an amount equal to the change in C.

4. $y = 2, x = -3$

5. **a.** $y = 2, x = 0$ **b.** $y = 0, x = 2$ **c.** $y = 3, x = 2$ **d.** $y = -3, x = -2$

6. **a.** $y = \frac{10}{x - 3} + 2$ **b.** $y = \frac{10}{x - 5} - 3$ **c.** $y = \frac{5}{x + 4} - 5$

Sine Function Match

For Use With Lesson 13-4

FILES NEEDED: Transformation Graphing App
Program: **A2L134**

A2L134 graphs the general form of the sine function $y = a \sin (b(x - c)) + d$, sometimes called a *sinusoid*, as Y1 = A sin(B(X − C)) + D.

In this activity you see three sine curves, one at a time. You are to change the values of **A** and **B** to find a perfect match for each given curve. Make sure that your graphing calculator is in **Radian** mode.

1. Run **A2L134**. What is the scale along the *x*-axis? Along the *y*-axis? Change values for **A** and **B** to find a sine function whose graph matches the given curve. Write the equation of this function.

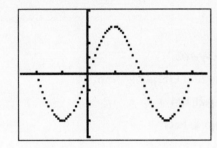

2. Switch from **Plot1** to **Plot2**. Press GRAPH to see the second curve. Find a sine function whose graph matches the given curve. Then write the equation.

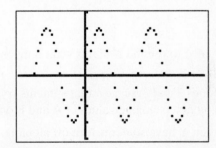

3. Switch from **Plot2** to **Plot3**. Press GRAPH to see the third curve. Find a sine function whose graph matches the given curve. Write the equation.

4. Turn off all Plots. Set **A** = 2 and **B** = 1. Predict the effects that changes in **C** and **D** will have on the graph. (You've seen these effects before!) Test your predictions.

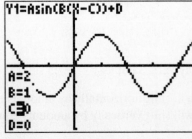

Extension

5. Use what you discovered in Question 4. Change the value of one of the parameters to translate the graph onto itself. List all values of the parameter for which you can do this.

Sine Function Match

Activity Objective

Students use the Transformation Graphing App to study the effects of changes in the values of *a* and *b* on the amplitude and wave length of the graph of the sinusoid $y = a \sin (b(x - c)) + d$.

Correlation to Text

- Lesson 13-4: The Sine Function

Time

- 20–25 minutes

Materials/Software

- Transformation Graphing App
- Program: **A2L134**
- Activity worksheet

Skills Needed

- change parameter values
- select and deselect a plot

Notes

- You may need to remind students what it means for a scale to be in radians.
- For Questions 2 and 3, suggest that students try to match the functions by first changing values of **A** and **B** only.
- For Question 4, have students turn off all plots.
- When changing values of **C**, remind students to use multiples of π.

Answers

1. $\frac{\pi}{2}, \pi, \frac{3\pi}{2}, \ldots ; 1, 2, 3, \ldots ; y = 3 \sin x$

2. $y = 3 \sin 2x$

3. Answers may vary. Sample: $y = -1.5 \sin 0.5x$

4. The graph will shift horizontally by amounts equal to the changes in **C**.
   The graph will shift vertically by amounts equal to the changes in **D**.

5. You can change **C** by any multiple of 2π and translate the graph onto itself.

Cosine Function Match

For Use With Lesson 13-7

> **FILES NEEDED:** Transformation Graphing App
> Program: **A2L137A**

A2L137A graphs the general form of the cosine function $y = a \cos(b(x - c)) + d$
as Y1 = A cos(B(X − C)) + D.

In this activity you see three cosine curves, one at a time. You are to change
the values of the parameters A, B, C, and D to find a perfect match for each
given curve. Make sure that your graphing calculator is in **Radian** mode.

1. Run **A2L137A**. What is the scale along the
x-axis? Along the y-axis? Change values of
the parameters to find a cosine function
whose graph matches the given curve. Write
the equation of the function.

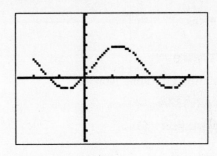

2. Switch from **Plot1** to **Plot2**. Press GRAPH to see the second curve.
Find a cosine function whose graph matches the given curve. Write
the equation.

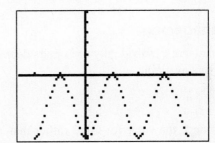

3. Switch from **Plot2** to **Plot3**. Press GRAPH
to see the third curve. Find a matching
cosine function.

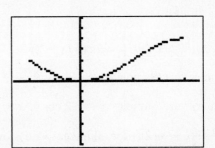

Extension

4. The sine function $y = \sin x$ and the cosine
function $y = \cos x$ appear to be translations of
each other. Show that this is true by finding the
phase shift (value of c) that gives identical
graphs for $y = \cos(x - c)$ and $y = \sin x$. List all
such phase shifts.

Cosine Function Match

Activity Objective

Students use the Transformation Graphing App to study the effects of changes in the values of $a, b, c,$ and d on the graph of the cosine function $y = a \cos (b(x - c)) + d$.

Correlation to Text

- Lesson 13-7: Translating Sine and Cosine Functions

Time

- 25–30 minutes

Materials/Software

- Transformation Graphing App
- Program: A2L137A
- Activity worksheet

Skills Needed

- change parameter values
- select and deselect a plot

Classroom Management

- Students can work individually or in pairs depending on the number of calculators available.

Notes

- For Question 1, the value for C is 2 rather than a multiple of π.

Answers

1. $\frac{\pi}{2}, \pi, \frac{3\pi}{2}, \ldots; 1, 2, 3, \ldots; y = 2 \cos (x - 2) + 1$

2. Answer may vary. Samples: $y = -3 \cos 2x - 3$ or $y = 3 \cos (2x - \pi) - 3$

3. Answer may vary. Samples: $y = -2 \cos 0.5x + 2$ or $y = 2 \cos (0.5x - \pi) + 2$

4. $c = \frac{\pi}{2}; c = \frac{\pi}{2} + n(2\pi)$ for all integer values of n.

Daylight Model

> **FILES NEEDED:** Transformation Graphing App
> Program: **A2L137B**

Run A2L137B. The startup screen plots hours of daylight in San Francisco, California, against the days of the year.

1. Write a short paragraph describing what happens to the number of daylight hours in San Francisco over one year.

2. Study the pattern of the plotted points. Of the functions you have studied so far—linear, absolute value, quadratic, radical, exponential, rational, and trigonometric—which do you think would make the best model for the relationship between the hours of daylight and the days of the year. Explain.

3. On the Y= screen, select the given sine function. (Highlight the "=" sign and press ENTER .) Press GRAPH . Change the values of the parameters A, B, C, D to find a sine function, $y = a \sin (b(x - c)) + d$, that is a good model for the data. Express A to one decimal place and B to three decimal places. When you feel you have a good model, zoom in to get a closer view. Refine your model if needed.

4. Use your model. In San Francisco, how long is the "longest day"? The shortest day? Today?

5. Activate both Plot1 and Plot2. Press GRAPH to see daylight data for both San Francisco and Anchorage, Alaska. Describe and explain the differences and similarities in the two plots.

6. Find a sine function model for the Anchorage data.

7. How much longer is the longest day in Anchorage than the longest day in San Francisco? How many days in Anchorage are longer than the longest day in San Francisco?

8. Predict differences you would expect to see in these plots and a plot for Sydney, Australia. Explain your predictions. Activate Plot3 and press GRAPH to see a plot for Sydney.

9. Why is the plot for Sydney "upside down"?

10. The data sets for the three cities "intersect" twice. Why? On what days does this happen? How long are these days?

11. In your sine models, what is the meaning of the value of D?

Extension

12. Use local resources and develop a model for your hometown. For your model, which of the parameters, A, B, C, and D would have the same values as for San Francisco, Anchorage, or Sydney?

Algebra 2

Daylight Model

Activity Objective

Students use the Transformation Graphing App to make a sine-curve model of the hours of daylight over a year.

Correlation to Text

- Lesson 13-7: Translating Sine and Cosine Functions

Time

- 40–50 minutes

Materials/Software

- Transformation Graphing App
- Program: **A2L137B**
- Activity worksheet

Skills Needed

- change parameter values
- select and deselect a plot

Notes

- Discuss with the students the use of the word *equinox*.

- Question 11 asks about the meaning of the value for D. You may wish to discuss why a good estimate for B is $\frac{2\pi}{365}$ and why a good estimate for C is 81 (the number of days from January 1 to March 22).

Answers

1. Answers may vary. Sample: The number of hours increase and then decrease.

2. Trigonometric; the plot suggests a sine function.

3. Answers may vary. Sample: $y = 2.6 \sin (0.017(x - 81)) + 12$

4. Answers based on the answer for Question 3. longest day: about 14.6 h; shortest day: about 9.4 h

5. Both sets of data follow a sine curve. Daylight hours for Anchorage are fewer in winter and greater in summer.

6. Answers may vary. Sample: $y = 6.8 \sin (0.017(x - 81)) + 12$

7. about 4.2 h; about 137 days

8. Sidney will have longer days when Anchorage and San Francisco have shorter ones.

9. Sidney is in the Southern Hemisphere

10. On about March 22 and September 22, all three cities have about 12 h of daylight.

11. D is the average length of a day, which is 12 h.

12. Check students' work; The parameter values for B, C, and D will be the same.

TI Connect™ Software System Requirements

For Windows®

- PC Operating System: Microsoft Windows® 98, NT 4.x, 2000 or ME, and XP Operating Systems. For Windows® 95 operating system users, note that TI Connect will work; however, some graphics may not appear correctly.

- Hard Disk Space: At least 15 MB available.

- Web Browser: Microsoft Internet Explorer 5.0 or greater may be required for functions that require use of your existing Internet connection.

For Macintosh®

- Processor: Macintosh® with 68020 or later processor, or PowerPC.

- Operating System: Macintosh OS 7.5.5 or later (including OS 9.2.2, OS X under Classic environment).

- RAM: At least 4 MB (preferably 8 MB).

- Hard Disk Space: At least 5 MB space available.

- Port:

  ► To support TI-GRAPH LINK™ Serial cable (Gray): Serial communications port (including Modem or Printer port, or combined Modem/Printer port on Powerbooks).

  ► To support TI-GRAPH LINK USB cable: Available USB port (OS 8.6 or later required).

- Scripting: Applescript 1.1 installed and enabled, prior to installing TI Connect software.

- Web Support: Mac® OS 8.6 or later required, Microsoft Internet Explorer 3.0 or later, or Netscape 3.0 or later may be required to view some documentation.